The Greening of Business:
Solar as a Bridge to our
Hydrogen-Electricity Future

George S. Howard, Ph.D.
University of Notre Dame

Other books by George S. Howard, Ph.D.

Basic Research Methods in the Social Sciences

Dare We Develop a Human Science?

A Tale of Two Stories: A Narrative Approach to Psychology

Understanding Human Nature: An Owner's Manual

Adaptive Counseling and Therapy: A Metatheoretical Approach (with Don Nance & Pennie Myers)

Issues in Alcohol Use and Misuse By Young Adults (with Peter Nathan)

UFOs and Alien Abduction: Two Centuries of Conflict (with Robert Bartholemew)

Ecological Psychology: Creating a More Earth-Friendly Human Nature

How Should I Lead My Life? Psychology, Environmental Science, and Moral Traditions

For the Love of Teaching

When Things Begin to Go Bad (with Edward Delgado-Romero)

Stan Ovshinsky and the Hydrogen Economy: Creating a Better World

The Greening of Business: Solar as a Bridge to our Hydrogen-Electricity Future

George S. Howard, Ph.D.
University of Notre Dame

Academic Publications
Box 187
Notre Dame, IN 46556

Published by Academic Publications,
Box 187, Notre Dame, IN 46556

Library of Congress Cataloging In Publication Data
    Howard, George S.
The Greening of Business: Solar as a Bridge to Our Hydrogen-
Electricity Future

ISBN 978-0-937647-06-6

    1. Science
    2. Hydrogen-Electric Economy
    3. Environment
    4. Politics

Printed in the United States of America

Cover design by John Cernak
Book design by John Cernak

Thanks is extended to Academic Publications for permission to
reprint, in Appendices 2-4, G. S. Howard (2006) "A new science,"
"Photovoltaics," and "25/30 MW Ovonic Roll-to-Roll PV
Manufacturing Machines" in *Stan Ovshinsky and the hydrogen economy:
Creating a better world*. Notre Dame, IN: Academic Publications.

Dedicated to:

Stanford R. Ovshinsky

The Father of the Hydrogen Economy
and
Co-Founder of *Energy Conversion Devices*

and

Tom Kanczuzewski

The Greenest Businessman I Know
and
Founder of *Inovateus Development*

Table of Contents

Foreword

A Time for Vision

Now is the time for vision. Energy issues have come into sharp focus over the last decade. It is now completely clear that we need a vision where looming problems (e.g., global warming, pollution-produced health problems, politically unstable energy sources, ill-advised foreign wars, monstrous balance of trade outflows, dizzying gasoline and electricity costs, and so forth) no longer threaten our future. Escaping such difficulties will likely require far more than the extrapolation of current trends. "More of the same" simply will not address our difficulties. An adequate solution requires a different approach from the familiar, hydrocarbon-burning past that we understand so well.

Still, it takes courage to push off from our safe, present energy system into the uncharted waters of new energy systems such as totally electric or hydrogen ones fueled by clean and renewable energy sources, like solar, wind and geothermal. William James was perhaps America's foremost philosopher and psychologist. His advice on how to understand and deal with the fear and uncertainty of radical changes is legendary.

> ....In all important transactions of life we have to take a leap in the dark....Each must act as he (sic) thinks best; and if he is wrong, so much the worse for him. We stand on a mountain pass in the midst of whirling snow and blinding mist, through which we get glimpses now and then of paths which may be deceptive. If we stand still we shall be frozen to death. If we take the wrong road we shall be dashed to pieces. We do not certainly know whether there is any right way. What must we do? Be strong and of good courage. Act for the best, hope for the best, and take what comes....If death ends all, we cannot meet death better. (*James*, 1897/1956, pp. 30-31)

So be strong and show courage, gentle reader, for our uncertain future is best faced with courage.

Certain that our current energy and environmental situations require a shift from the hydrocarbon economy, Professor Howard discusses various elements of possible energy futures for our consideration, tracing their strengths and liabilities. In our democracy, politicians will promote energy solutions and will appeal for our votes based in part on their vision. Business and industry will lead in developing the components of these energy futures. We deserve political representatives and business leaders who understand energy issues far more deeply than special interest groups often portray these issues. We live in a highly politicized age, a time when many make anti-environmental claims backed by only superficial justifications or opinions (e.g., "Moving away from burning hydrocarbons will cost American jobs," "We will never run out of oil"). By truly understanding the issues, we can persuade others to more closely examine the facts and challenge inaccuracies.

The more people are challenged to address the validity of their assertions, the less often uninformed opinions and assertions will clutter important environmental discussions and future decision-making regarding our energy future. There are truths in this world—some scientific, others religious—that ought to guide our actions. Where special interests alone reign, the truth inevitably suffers. No one ever said democracy would be easy. In these political times, this book is a good way to begin educating yourself about our possible energy futures, for the future is best faced with accurate knowledge and understanding.

I believe that one of the finest examples of New Testament theology can be found in the Beatitudes which Jesus gave to us in his Sermon on the Mount. The Beatitudes express profound truths like, "Blessed are the poor in spirit, for theirs is the kingdom of heaven" and "Blessed are the peacemakers, for they shall be called children of God." I sometimes teasingly accuse Professor Howard of trying to add a ninth beatitude to the Lord's original eight, "Blessed are the mathematically competent, for they shall save the earth." Many of Howard's points are made mathematically. Not through difficult mathematics like Calculus, Differential Equations or Mathematical Modeling, but with simple arithmetic calculations. Unfortunately, many readers skim over paragraphs containing calculations. Please don't. I urge you to redouble your efforts to carefully understand the calculations herein. Your efforts will be amply rewarded.

I recently celebrated my ninetieth birthday. God has been generous in granting me longevity. Sadly, my eyes have failed me more with each passing year. However, the decline in one's sight tends to sharpen other modes of vision. God has given each of us the vision of the mind, of the heart, and of the soul. There has never been a better time for us to exercise as many of these forms of vision as God has given us. Now is the time for vision—the vision of an improved energy system, one that is completely clean and renewable.

Theodore M. Hesburgh, C.S.C.
President Emeritus, University of Notre Dame

Introduction

Over the last five years, I have had the opportunity to work with a number of politicians and business leaders who are concerned about our current energy problems and about the solutions to our future energy needs. In these interactions, I have been impressed with their sincere desire to be effective agents of change and their willingness to venture into the numerous and sometimes confusing technologies of the future. I decided to compile information that I have found useful in understanding the issues involved in the transition from our present energy systems (that rely on polluting, non-renewable energy sources) to the necessary clean and renewable energy systems of the future.

In 2007, Iain Carson and Vijay Vaitheeswaran wrote *Zoom: The global race to fuel the car of the future*. That book gave a thorough history of the transition from hydrocarbon-powered vehicles to a projection of hybrid, electric, and hydrogen-powered vehicles in our future. *The greening of business: Solar as a bridge to our hydrogen-electricity future* considers how we heat, cool, power and light our factories, offices, and homes. That is, it focuses on stationary applications in the coming hydrogen-electricity economy.[1]

Geoffrey Ballard predicted society was in the process of slowly abandoning the burning of hydrocarbons to obtain power. In its place would arise the age of hydricity (i.e., the hydrogen-electricity economy). While coal, oil, or natural gas can be burned to produce energy, such reactions are non-reversible (one cannot take energy and convert it back into coal, oil, or gas). However, hydrogen-electricity transactions are reversible. Feed electricity into water and one obtains hydrogen; feed hydrogen into a fuel cell and one obtains electricity and water. Reversibility will make the hydrogen-electricity economy more flexible than our current hydrocarbon-powered economy. This

---

[1] Oil is the dominant fuel for *Zoom*'s transportation applications. For stationary applications, coal and natural gas are the hydrocarbon partners with oil. *Big coal* by Jeff Goodell offers a history of coal use that is comparable to *Zoom*'s history of oil use for transportation applications.

is but one of the several benefits to moving away from the burning of hydrocarbons to power our factories, offices, and homes. Other benefits are that renewable sources of energy (e.g., solar, wind, geothermal) can be used. Finally, these new sources of energy and hydrogen-electricity transactions do not produce pollution, nor do they generate greenhouse gases. It's a wonderful, new world we are moving toward.

In Fall, 2007, the U.S. House of Representatives sent a very good bill to the Senate for approval. Instead of approving it and sending the bill to the President, the Senate added amendments that seriously weakened the bill. The Energy Bill of 2007 still had the increased average mileage for auto fleets, a new round of incentives for corn ethanol, and a nice push toward cellulostic ethanol. These provisions involved transportation applications. I believe that *Zoom* played a role in keeping the transportation applications at the forefront of our legislators' minds.

The part of the bill that was gutted applied to stationary applications (e.g., houses, factories, offices). The national RES (renewable energy standard) was dropped. Much needed incentives for alternative energy sources, like wind and solar, were dropped. Also, the repeal of some recent additional incentives given to hydrocarbon companies was dropped. These dropped portions of the Energy Bill of 2007 will be proposed again soon. Perhaps this book can do for stationary applications what *Zoom* did for transportation applications.

Chapter 1

How I Got Started...

Ricky climbed into the passenger seat as I slid behind the wheel. We were in the parking lot of *Energy Conversion Devices* (*ECD*). The doors slammed shut. We glanced at one another and burst into uproarious laughter. It was the pressure of six hours of having to stifle our laughter that made the outbursts so explosive. After several minutes of release, we began to settle in for the long ride home.

"Could you believe the stuff Stan Ovshinsky was telling us?" Ricky began.

"No way," I replied. "And it's so sad because it's such a waste of good science..."

"Wait!" Ricky shouted. "You liked the science? How real is it? You actually liked the science?"

"Of course I liked it," I shot back. "What's not to like? Through atomic engineering, they've found ways of creating new materials from combinations of chemicals. These new materials possess physical characteristics that no materials before them have possessed. What's not to like about that?"

"You bought all that amorphous stuff? You really think that stuff works?"

"I'm not a physicist or materials science guy, but the articles were published in great places like *Nature, Journal of Applied Physics, Scientific American, Physical Review Letters* and *IEEE Transactions*. Besides, the ideas have been out there for over forty years. Hoaxes don't stand the test of scientific scrutiny for long. They sniffed out Cold Fusion in a matter of months. No, I'd be very surprised if the science is bogus. I'll check it out with some chemists and electrical engineers, but I'm pretty sure it's good science."

Ricky softly muttered, "Oh, man."

Ricky Behrman was a business major and one of the smartest students I've encountered in my thirty years of higher education. After several years as a portfolio manager at *Fidelity* investments, he returned to graduate work in business at Harvard. I was a professor of environmental psychology. After a few minutes of silence, Ricky spoke again,

"Professor, if the science is good, what were *you* laughing at?"

"Oh Ricky," I began impatiently, "as a company, *Energy Conversion Devices* is a joke! The building was a shanty..."

"You want them spending stockholders' money on overhead?" Ricky roared.

"No, not exactly, but every building we went into was a completely different industry—batteries, photovoltaics, computer chips, DVDs, solid hydrogen storage, fuel cells. How does it all fit together?"

"Actually, I liked the business model," Ricky replied. "*ECD* is not only a research and development outfit. It seems that virtually every discovery they make has implications for most of their businesses. Think of *ECD* as a wheel with spokes. The science occurs in the middle and then breakthroughs radiate out to each of their businesses. One discovery that changes seven different businesses in seven different ways is as good as seven discoveries—isn't it? I just wondered about the science..."

"Ricky," I interrupted impatiently, "forty years without a profit. What kind of idiot would buy into a business plan like that?"

"Me," Ricky volunteered confidently. "If the science is good, I'm ready to buy. I think you're looking at those losses all wrong. Somebody else has already booked those losses. And what do you— by investing now—get for all those losses? Buying stock now buys you a share of a mountain of intellectual property. You know, those hundreds of American patents, they're carrying them on the books at $0 value—zero! If their science is good, the barriers to entry for competitors are enormous. I was laughing because I thought the science was flaky."

"No, the science is probably fine," I muttered. "So you really like their business model?"

"Yes, I do. I think they'll sell product once their markets mature sufficiently—you know, hybrid electric autos, fuel cells, photovoltaics, Ovonic memory chips. I'm more worried about their access to the credit markets. They'd better turn a profit soon or..."

"Wait a minute," I stammered. "You really like their business model?"

"What's not to like? They're targeting multi-billion dollar markets. They have a science and technologies that you're telling me are good. Their intellectual property poses an almost insurmountable barrier to entry for competitors. And they're doing all this on a shoestring budget. I could be wrong, but I think I've fallen in love with their business plan."

"Wow," was all I could say.

I've made the drive from Detroit, Michigan to South Bend, Indiana many times. That trip home in 1999 was perhaps the most intellectually exciting three hours of my life. Meeting Stan and Iris Ovshinsky and learning about *ECD* was like taking a step into the future.

How One Punctuates Time

How one chooses to punctuate time is a crucial aspect of any story. I highlighted an April day in 1999 as my starting point. However, very different beginnings are also possible. While my ride with Ricky was a very subjective beginning, Table 1-1 strives to provide a more objective timeline for the shift from our hydrocarbon economy toward a new hydrogen-electricity economy.

Table 1-1

Events Leading to the Rise of Alternative Energy

1750   The Industrial Revolution begins in England with the mining of coal to produce steam.

1798   Reverend Thomas Malthus publishes *An essay on the principle of population.*

1859   Oil is discovered in Pennsylvania.

1897   With the end of the Depression of 1893, recoveries in timber, coal, iron, railroads, etc. push the hydrocarbon economy into high gear in America.

1929   The Great Depression begins.

1941   World War II reignites geometric growth in the burning of hydrocarbons.

1960   Stan and Iris Ovshinsky found *Energy Conversion Devices* (*ECD*).

1962   Rachel Carson publishes *Silent spring* and launches the environmental movement in America.

1967   The California Air Resources Board is formed.

1970   The Environmental Protection Agency is established.

1990   *GM*'s EV-1 uses hydrogen in *ECD*'s battery to propel autos for the first time.

2003   *ECD*'s first Auburn Hills 30MW/year photovoltaic cell production plant goes into operation.

2005   President George W. Bush signs the Energy Act of 2005 which lavishes billions of dollars on the hydrocarbon industries of the past.

2006   Tom Kanczuzewski founds *Inovateus Development*

2006   California passes its "Million Solar Roofs" legislation.

2007   Congress passes the badly flawed Energy Bill of 2007.

Because I wrote the biography of Stanford Ovshinsky (Howard, 2006), I know *ECD*'s contributions to the genesis of the hydrogen-electricity economy quite well. Another writer might highlight: Geoffrey Ballard's founding of *Ballard Power*; *BP Amoco*'s move into solar power; *GE*'s move into the production of wind turbines and solar cells; and the like. The next chapter provides an overview of why our current energy and environmental situations require this shift from the hydrocarbon economy. In all likelihood, we are in the last decades of the hydrocarbon economy and the beginnings of … What?

Chapter 2

The Energy Problem

Most of the power required for our modern economy is produced by burning hydrocarbons.[2] Some hydrocarbons are superior fuel sources to others in terms of the lower quantity of pollutants produced and the lesser amount of greenhouse gases released per unit of heat generated. This advantage is due to the number of hydrogen atoms relative to the number of carbon atoms in the hydrocarbon molecule. The more hydrogen atoms per carbon atom, the better. Imagine a molecule that bonded two hydrogen atoms to one carbon atom. It's H/C ratio would be 2. This hypothetical molecule would likely be *superior* to wood (H/C =.30) and coal (H/C =1.3) in the lesser amount of pollutants and green house gases produced. Conversely, the H/C ratio of 2 makes this hypothetical molecule *inferior* to natural gas (H/C = 4) in the amount of pollutants and greenhouse gases produced. This molecule you've imagined would be oil (H/C=2).

For tens of thousands of years the burning of wood was humans' chief source of heat. Around 1780, in England, coal replaced wood because it was a better energy source (wood's H/C is .30 while coal has an H/C ratio of 1.3) and the Industrial Revolution began. Eventually coal gave way to oil and finally to natural gas as our evolution toward the use of superior hydrocarbon energy sources progressed. Below we take a look at the connections between our present energy systems and emerging environmental problems.

What Makes Something Environmentally Problematic or Helpful to an Ecosystem?

There are many ways to tell scientific tales of the future. Perhaps the least controversial approach is simply to state current scientific theories and to plot the present trends of the variables implicated as

---

[2] There are other power sources (e.g., hydro-electric power, nuclear power) that supplement the power obtained by burning hydrocarbons.

important by those theories. Paul Ehrlich and Ann Ehrlich (1990) noted that the stress placed upon any ecosystem by humans can be determined by consulting the following formula, $I = P \times A \times T$ or $I = PAT$. In this formulation, the impact (I) of any group is the product of the size of its population (P), its per-capita level of affluence (A) as measured by consumption of goods and services, and a measure of the damage done by the technologies (T) employed in supplying each unit of that consumption. An ecosystem's carrying capacity is defined as the population size that an ecosystem can sustain indefinitely. When the human population's total impact (I) exceeds the ecosystem's sustainable carrying capacity, the ecosystem begins to deteriorate. Unless human impact is reduced, an ecosystem pushed beyond its carrying capacity will deteriorate until it eventually crashes.

Let's take a closer look at these variables. Counting the number of humans in a population is a reasonably straightforward task, and so, determining the value of P is relatively easy. Figure 2-1, shows the course of P over the last thousand years. Any person who examines this graph will realize that our species is now experiencing out-of-control growth. The results of this growth might be catastrophic for the health of our planet's ecosystems.

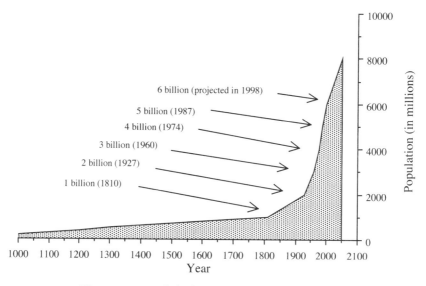

Figure 2-1. Global population growth.

Measuring the population's affluence level (A) is much more difficult because combining entities such as land, water, air, energy, and so forth into one overall measure is problematic. GDP (Gross Domestic Product) has traditionally been used to measure a population's level of affluence (A). The technology (T) term is often mistakenly thought to signify an anti-technology bias in the I = PAT equation. However, T simply reflects the environmental *destructiveness* of the techniques used to produce the goods and services consumed. In fact, sophisticated technologies can obtain either high or low values assigned for T.

For example, complex technologies, such as nuclear powered electric plants, can have high values for T because society cannot safely deal with radioactive waste for the thousands of years that it requires attention. Similarly, chlorofluorocarbons (CFCs) used as aerosol propellants, as cleaning detergents for microprocessors, and for heat transfer in cooling units once were considered to be commodities with a low assigned value of T. But CFCs' value for T first increased when they were found to be greenhouse gases, and then increased again when they were implicated in the destruction of the earth's ozone layer, which protects us from the sun's ultraviolet rays. Thus, the value assigned for T is always a function of the scientific state of knowledge of the entities and techniques in question. In a later chapter we consider a very complex technology—photovoltaic cells—that produces electricity and has a value for T of about zero.

Unfortunately, there is currently no accepted procedure for obtaining worldwide values for T. Values can be estimated only on a technology-by-technology basis. However, several scientists have suggested that a measure of a population's energy consumption serves as the best available index of the combination of affluence and technology (A x T) for our hydrocarbon economy. This is because several disparate entities (e.g., forests lost, oil burned) can be converted into energy unit equivalents with little distortion. Also, the amount of waste produced by human activities is now closely related to the amount of carbon-based energy consumed. What energy consumption (as a measure of A x T) hides is the fact that not all sources of energy stress ecosystems equally. For example, obtaining electricity from solar power stresses the earth far, far less than obtaining electricity by burning coal. What are the current paths of P, A, and energy consumption (A x T) in the above I = PAT formula?

I know of no worldwide figures of the growth in energy consumption and GDP. However, the growth in energy consumption, GDP, and population in developing countries over a 30-year period is shown in Figure 2-2.

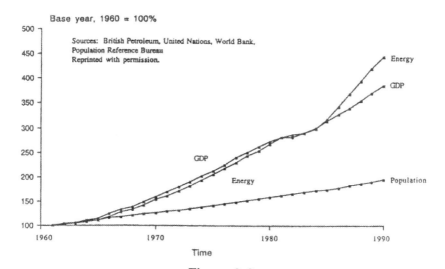

Figure 2-2.
Thirty year increases in energy consumption, GDP, and population.

Although a 30-year time span might be large for some studies, it represents a deceptively short span for the physical and biological trends that now threaten the planet. As with all restriction of range problems, one tends to underestimate the magnitude and importance of relations when they are assessed during a narrow window of time. Thus, population, GDP, and energy use appear to grow in a *linear* fashion as shown in Figure 2-2. Similarly, the standardization procedure performed on the dependent measures (using 1960 as the base year) in Figure 2-2 also tends to make the trends appear less dramatic than if the raw data had been presented. However, the trajectory of growth in the global human population can be interpreted as a *geometric* (or exponential) trend when considered over a much longer period of time—such as the last thousand years (See Figure 2-1). In reality, the increases in GDP and energy consumption in Figure 2-2 are even *steeper* than the growth in population depicted in Figure 2-1. Since the Industrial Revolution, the planet's human population (P) and the amount of energy consumed by humans (A x T) have increased geometrically. This represents an inherently unstable situation that must be corrected. Kenneth Boulding, former president of the American Economic Association, stated the problem succinctly, "Only madmen and economists believe in *perpetual* exponential growth." (See Appendix 1, "Too Many People").

All of this is to reinforce the fact that growth in P and A has been staggering over the last thousand years. Our ecosystems are condemned to succumb to the stress (I) we place on them unless we dramatically lower the T-term in the I = PAT formula.

In a book that considers the gamut of environmental problems, Esty and Winston (2007) rank order our present environmental challenges, as shown in Table 2-1 below.

Table 2-1

Top 10 Environmental Problems

1. **Climate Change**: The build-up of greenhouse gases in the atmosphere threatens to lead to global warming and the accompanying rising sea levels, changed rainfall patterns, and increased intensity of storms.

2. **Energy**: A carbon-constrained future will require a shift toward new modes of power generation and sustainable energy or new technologies for cleanly burning fossil fuels.

3. **Water**: Water-quality issues and water shortages are threatening licenses to operate and constraining business activities all around the globe.

4. **Biodiversity and Land Use**: Ecosystems play a critical role as life support for both humans and nature. Unmanaged development undermines this capacity through habitat destruction, loss of open space, and species decline.

5. **Chemicals, Toxins, and Heavy Metals**: These contaminants create a risk of cancer, reproductive harm, and other health issues in humans, plants, and animals.

6. **Air Pollution**: Smog, particulates, and volatile organic compounds pose a risk to public health, especially in the developing world where trends are worsening. Indoor air pollution is now recognized as an added problem.

7. **Waste Management**: Many communities still struggle with the disposal of their solid and toxic waste, especially in countries that are industrializing and becoming more urban.

8. **Ozone Layer Depletion**: Depletion has been substantially reduced by phasing out CFCs, but some substitutes continue to cause thinning of the Earth's protective ozone shield.

9. **Oceans and Fisheries**: Overfishing, pollution, and climate change have depleted fish stocks and damaged marine ecosystems across the Seven Seas.

10. **Deforestation**: Unsustainable timber harvesting plagues many parts of the world, leading to soil erosion, water pollution, increased risk of flooding, and scarred landscapes.

The technological solution to defeat the top two issues is currently available. All that remains is to gear up the nation's productive capacities to produce the products (i.e., solar cells, wind turbines, geothermal units, etc.) needed to convert sunlight (either directly, or as wind, or as heat) into electricity. These fledgling industries will provide the tens (perhaps hundreds) of thousands of high quality jobs that America needs to replace the positions lost through the demise of our hydrocarbon economy. If we do not seize these new industries now, our Asian and European competitors will be all too happy to take them from us. Finally, why would we go to war to protect oil supplies in the Persian Gulf when the sun will give us all the electricity we require?

The next chapter examines several examples whereby we might improve upon our present hydrocarbon economy in order to minimize its debilitating impact on the environment. In so doing, we can extend the "usable life" of our present energy system even while moving into the age of hydricity (hydrogen-electricity). The remaining chapters in this book discuss the technological, business, political, and other issues involved in developing the alternative energy solutions we need.

Chapter 3

While In Transition...

Today a confluence of factors (e.g., peak oil, pollution problems, rising CO_2 levels producing global warming, hydrocarbon sources residing in politically unstable parts of the world) suggest we might be nearing the end of the age of burning hydrocarbons to power our economy. However, even as we look for viable alternative energy solutions for our future, we will still be umbilically tied to our hydrocarbon economy for many years to come. We must do everything in our power to minimize the negative consequences of burning hydrocarbons. Below are four effective ways to conserve energy and thus improve our use of hydrocarbons.

1. When the Lightbulb Finally Goes On

"You catch more flies with honey then you do with vinegar," is a maxim I heard growing up. Did you hear that the Energy Bill of 2007 will soon outlaw the sale of incandescent lightbulbs because they waste so much electricity relative to compact fluorescents? Unfortunately, Americans hate to be told *not* to do something, so the government might be using vinegar when they could use honey. In this case, honey is money. Would you like to hear the most spectacular, practical money-saving tip I've ever heard?

My local store will sell me a *GE* 26w compact fluorescent lightbulb for $2.53 or a comparable *GE* 100w incandescent bulb for $.94. The incandescent bulb lasts 1/10th as long as the compact fluorescent. If a light is on for seven hours each day, the compact fluorescent bulb will burn out in about four years as will ten incandescent bulbs.

The materials cost for the compact fluorescent bulb is $2.53 whereas it is $9.40 for 10 incandescent bulbs. Electricity costs $23.40 for the compact fluorescent and $90 for the incandescents (using the national average of $.09 per kw hr). Your extra investment at the time of purchase of the compact fluorescent is a paltry $1.59. What savings do you obtain over four years for this investment? The higher tech fluorescent bulb saves you $73.47 [(9.40+90)-(2.53+23.40)] over the four years.

Since your initial investment was only an additional $1.59, your guaranteed, tax free, rate of return on the investment is 4600% ($73.47 / 1.59 x 100). A forty-six hundred percent tax-free rate of return on your investment over four years (or 1150% per anum) is mind-boggling. Now count up the number of incandescent lightbulbs in your home and head to *Wal-Mart*, or *Target*, or *Meijers*, or *Home Depot*, or *Lowes*, and invest wisely.

More importantly, you spew out almost four times the pollution and greenhouse gases when you light your home using incandescent bulbs. It's small wonder that our government seeks to make incandescent bulbs illegal—they are that bad. If only we would talk more about that honey, people might stop throwing away their hard-earned money and start buying compact fluorescents.

Finally, each dollar you save by purchasing compact fluorescent bulbs is worth $1.75 earned. Remember the old saying, "A penny saved is a penny earned"? Sadly, it's incorrect. Imagine you want to buy a $1,000 sofa. How much money would you need to earn to buy that sofa? Well, if there is a 5% sales tax, you actually need $1,050 to buy the sofa. The question now is, "How much money must you earn to have $1,050 to spend?" If you are self-employed and successful, the following tax profile might fit you. Federal tax of 31%, 5% social security taxes, 3% state, and 1% county or city tax. In this case, you must pay 40% in taxes overall, and thus have 60% left to spend. If you earn $1,750 and get to keep only 60% of it, you have $1,050 (which is the real price of the sofa).

Therefore, to buy a $1,000 sofa you must earn $1,750. Analogously, a penny saved is 1 ¾ pennies earned. Now that is a deal you cannot afford to pass up.

2. Hybrid Automobiles

Virtually all autos run by burning gasoline. The burning takes place through tiny explosions in the motor's cylinders. The desired outcome is mechanical energy that can be used to accelerate the auto. The undesired products of the tiny explosions are pollutants (e.g.,

NO_x, SO_2) and greenhouse gases (e.g., CO_2) which escape through the auto's exhaust system.

Imagine you accelerate from a standing position to a speed of 60 mph. You have converted potential energy (in the gasoline) into kinetic energy (60 mph) and waste products. With a standard auto, if the light ahead turns red, you apply the brakes, which convert your kinetic energy into heat via friction of the brake shoes on the brake drums. This waste heat then dissipates. This is the reason that city mileage is generally lower than highway mileage for a standard auto. Every time you hit the brakes, you waste kinetic energy, rather than having the kinetic energy cover additional distance.

With a hybrid vehicle (such as *Toyota's Prius*), a small internal combustion engine very efficiently burns gasoline (which is why it is part of the hydrocarbon economy) to accelerate your auto. However, your hybrid also has a large battery and an electric motor which assists the gasoline motor in propelling the auto. Thus the *Prius* requires much less gasoline to accelerate from 0 to 60 mph than non-hybrid autos (in this way it produces less pollution and greenhouse gases). The question then is, "Why doesn't the battery run out of energy after several starts and stops?"

When your *Prius* reaches 60 mph and the light ahead turns red, you slow the car by having the kinetic energy produce electricity that is stored in the large battery. Rather than wasting kinetic energy through the braking system (as traditional cars do), the kinetic energy becomes electricity. Thus, when the light next turns green, part of your acceleration is accomplished by energy recaptured from your previous braking. This is like getting two bites out of an apple, which is always superior to taking only one bite of an apple (using gasoline to accelerate the auto initially) and then throwing the rest of the apple away (wasting kinetic energy through the traditional braking system). This process is called regenerative braking, and it is a large part of why hybrids actually get superior city mileage over highway mileage.

3. Cogeneration

Electricity is produced when steam power moves a dynamo through a strong electric field. As the steam cools, it condenses into very hot water which exits the electric plant. Often this "waste" water is put in a pond or lake where it cools. [Dissipating waste heat in this manner can have negative effects on the lake's ecosystem, but that is a discussion for another day.]

Many owners of electricity plants can put this "waste" heat to good use. For example the University of Notre Dame produces electricity, especially during peak (daytime) hours. Rather than dissipating its waste heat in a lake, it is used to heat the overwhelming majority of buildings on campus. Remarkably, in summer the "waste" heat can be used to cool those same buildings through a process known as evaporative cooling. By using the steam from its boilers to first produce electricity, and then to heat (or cool) its buildings, the University of Notre Dame system's overall efficiency is remarkably high. By performing multiple tasks with its heat, the University minimizes the amount of pollution and greenhouse gases it produces when it burns hydrocarbons to power its energy system.

Cogeneration is another example of getting two bites out of an apple.

4. Saving Off-Peak Power

This final example of better use of hydrocarbon-produced energy actually unites aspects of the hydrocarbon and hydrogen-electricity economies. Off-peak (nighttime) electricity demand is far lower than peak time demand (daytime). But it is a bad idea to constantly turn power plants on and off. Thus, a large percentage of a utility's power plants run constantly. The number of plants constantly producing electricity (called base load plants) is largely determined by the peak electricity demand. Thus, more electricity is produced at night than is needed. Because electricity must be used immediately or stored, a good deal of nighttime electricity goes to waste. The environmental price has been paid (i.e., in pollutants and greenhouse gases), but no benefit secured from this wasted electricity. Is there any way to get a second bite out of this apple?

If one passes the excess electricity through water, hydrogen is produced and can easily be stored. The next day, the hydrogen can be burned (instead of coal, for example) to produce electricity. When hydrogen is burned, no pollutants or greenhouse gases are produced. However, it would be more efficient (i.e., generate more peak time electricity) to use the hydrogen to power a fuel cell. The products of the chemical reaction inside a fuel cell are electricity and the amount of water that you electrolyzed the night before. In this example, hydrocarbons are used to generate the electricity initially; thus this first process belongs to the hydrocarbon economy. The second part of the plan involves converting water into hydrogen, which will then satisfy our need for more electricity at a later time. This second process involves the hydrogen-electricity economy.

Chapter 4

The Alternative Energy Solution:
Hydrogen-Electricity

It is clear that electricity will be an even greater part of our future than it was a part of our past. Energy has always served as the life blood of our basic industries. However, in the past, vast amounts of that energy came from burning coal, oil and natural gas. Over time industries relied more and more on electricity to power factories, and will continue to do so. Furthermore, our transportation systems in the future will likely run on electricity or hydrogen—which is simply stored electricity—no more, no less.

Similarly, the information industries have witnessed spectacular growth since the middle of the 20th Century. At the start, the mechanical typewriter was this industry's workhorse machine. Its inputs came from people's brains and the mechanical energy from typists' fingers. People's thoughts were converted into marks on pieces of paper. No external sources of energy were required to make the transition from brain to paper [Although non-electric energy sources were required to produce the typewriter, the paper, and the human thoughts and keystrokes involved.]

This mechanical technology is not some relic out of our distant past. Until 2004, that was how I did my income taxes (my pencil substituted for a typewriter). But now I'm in the heart of the electricity age. I turn on my computer, call up my turbo tax, and convert the information in my mind into an electronic file which (with the press of a single button) magically flies (I assume electrons "fly" through cyberspace) into the possession of the IRS somewhere in the USA— or perhaps it now goes to India! [Truth be told, I still print out my tax return and mail the paper to the IRS in Kansas City. I know that doing so totally humiliates my sons, but you see I have this recurring nightmare of my electrons bumping into somebody else's electrons in cyberspace and my winding up in jail for underpayment of taxes. God, how I miss the 20th Century!]

The main point is that the amount of electricity we now consume is almost unbelievable, and in the future we'll need that much more. Thus, finding viable ways to generate the staggering amounts of electricity our society will need without crippling our planet's ecosystems is a most important task.

Here Comes the Sun

If there is one thing that is *not* likely to change in this world, it's what the sun charges for its light. Therein lies the overwhelming advantage of alternative energy sources over burning hydrocarbons — oil now costs over $100 a barrel while sunlight costs nothing, natural gas costs $8 per thousand cubic feet while sunlight costs nothing, coal sells for about $36 per ton while sunlight costs nothing, and so forth. Figure 4-1 presents an illustration of what Stanford Ovshinsky called "the hydrogen loop," which shows the interplay among components such as photovoltaics, batteries, fuel cells, solid hydrogen storage and electrolyzers.

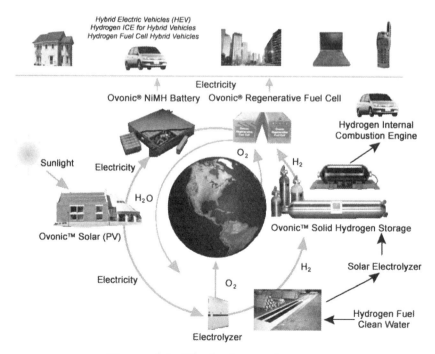

Figure 4-1. The hydrogen loop.

Simply stated, the sun is the sole energy source for this system. Ovonic thin film photovoltaic (PV) solar cells convert the sun's rays into electricity. The electricity can either be used immediately, stored in nickel-metal hydride (NiMH) batteries, or used to generate hydrogen from the electrolysis of water. Virtually any work can be accomplished with one or more of the above carriers of energy. Take, for example, the propulsion of an automobile. *General Motors'* EV-1 was a plug-in electric automobile. Electricity was delivered from its nickel-metal hydride battery to the electric motor that propelled the car. Or, for example, *ECD* has utilized its hydride powders to store hydrogen as a solid, thus replacing the gas tank of a hybrid automobile. Here, the internal combustion engine is run on hydrogen rather than gasoline. Together with its nickel-metal hydride batteries, it becomes an all-hydrogen car. Finally, hydrogen can be delivered to an Ovonic Regenerative Fuel Cell, which chemically converts the hydrogen gas back into electricity in a car. This electricity can then be used to run an electric motor which propels the automobile. A moment's reflection reveals that anything that burns—wood, coal, gasoline, or natural gas—can be replaced by hydrogen-electricity. One can appreciate that many important tasks (heating or cooling our offices and homes, running appliances, lighting, etc.) can also be accomplished this way.

A few important differences exist between these two types (hydrocarbon vs. hydrogen-electric) of energy systems. First, in the old energy system, conversions are generally non-reversible. While you can burn gasoline to provide momentum for your car, you can't then convert this momentum back into gasoline. While you can burn coal to produce electricity, the electricity can't then be used to create more coal. Finally, while natural gas can be burned to heat your home, one can't take left-over heat and use it to create natural gas. In the hydrocarbon economy, energy conversions generally go one—and only one—way. Thus, these energy sources are deemed non-reversible.

Conversely, in the hydrogen-electricity economy, most energy conversions are *reversible*. We encountered one in Chapter 3 when we explained how hybrid autos achieved their amazing mileage gains relative to hydrocarbon-age autos. With a hybrid auto, acceleration is produced by both the internal combustion engine and Stan Ovshinsky's nickel-metal hydride battery. Why was it important to use Stan's battery?

Stan's battery works by moving hydrogen from the anode (where it was stored when the battery was charged) to the cathode. This movement produces electricity, which, when routed through an electric motor, propels the car forward. The electric motor is aided by a small, extremely efficient internal combustion engine, which together accelerate the auto. Once you reach cruising speed, the electric system reverses and the car's momentum is used to move the hydrogen (now in the cathode) back to the anode. This process is accelerated when one steps on the brake, and, as noted before, is known as regenerative braking. In summary, you used electrochemical energy (stored in the anode of Stan's battery) to produce momentum. With regenerative braking, that momentum is used to recharge the battery, and thus is ready for reuse (which we called "getting a second bite of the apple"). One can clearly see that this is a reversible process.

Similarly, when light falls on Stan's amorphous, thin film photovoltaic cells, they produce electricity. If one routes electricity through a lightbulb, it produces light. Again, the system is reversible. Finally, if one sends electricity through water, it produces hydrogen and oxygen. When you use that hydrogen to power a fuel cell, you generate electricity (plus you get the water back). Again, reversibility is a characteristic of most transactions in hydrogen-electricity energy systems.

There are other natural advantages that hydrogen-electricity systems possess relative to our old strategy of burning hydrocarbons to produce energy. Burning hydrocarbons produces pollution of various sorts. Small particles (e.g., soot), NO_x, and SO_2 injure humans' physical health and the health of earth's ecosystems. Similarly, burning hydrocarbons releases CO_2, which is the principal greenhouse gas that is causing global warming. Conversely, *no pollutants* are produced in hydrogen-electricity conversions. Furthermore, *no greenhouse gases* are produced in hydrogen-electricity transformations.

Another advantage to dealing with hydrogen-electricity transactions is that the energy needed to power the system can easily be obtained from *renewable* energy sources (e.g., solar, wind, geothermal, tides). Hydrocarbons (e.g., oil, coal, natural gas) are generally non-renewable. However, we need not run out of a hydrocarbon for non-renewability to become a problem. With each hydrocarbon source, as soon as its commercial viability is established, the "low hanging fruit" is harvested first. M. King Hilbert's work on the Peak Oil phenomenon has demonstrated conclusively that severe economic (and environmental) disruptions occur when half of the hydrocarbon resource has been harvested. The price of the hydrocarbon can increase geometrically when the half-way point is reached. This is because fruit at the top of the tree is more expensive to harvest than the fruit we could pick while standing on the ground. For oil, in all likelihood, the earth's super-giant oil fields have already been discovered (most by the 1940s) and all are approaching or have passed their peaks. With every passing year, a greater percentage of oil used comes from deeper wells, tighter formations, more remote (from refineries and points of use) locations, and smaller oil pools. All of these factors conspire to dramatically increase the average cost of every barrel of oil produced. Ten years ago, a barrel of oil cost $20 on the world market; as I write, a barrel costs $102. Many (e.g., Simmons, 2006; Lerch, 2007) wager that recent cost increases are but the beginning of an irreversible, geometric trend.

Joining reversibility, its non-polluting nature, and renewability as advantages of hydrogen-electricity energy systems, is the fact that the newer energy systems are more naturally *distributed*. Hydrocarbon energy systems are naturally centralized. For example, burning coal to produce electricity in my home (where I use most of the electricity I "consume") is really not an option. Huge electricity generation plants represent the best solution for converting coal to electricity. The great cost and effort associated with building, maintaining, and operating the grid are then necessary to bring the centrally-produced electricity to my home—the point of use. Conversely, solar electricity can be produced at almost every point of use—it is naturally distributed. Wind and geothermal are a little less naturally distributed, while tides are not very naturally distributed at all.

The final advantage of a hydrogen-electricity energy system is that once the infrastructure is built (and, of course, maintained), the energy in the system costs nothing—as opposed to the spiraling costs of all fuels for hydrocarbon systems. In the United States, the infrastructure for converting coal, oil, natural gas, etc. into electricity is largely already built and paid for. A combination of corporate and government resources constructed that system. I recommend that the same corporate-government coalition build the infrastructure for the hydrogen-electricity economy. Thus, photovoltaic cells, wind turbines, tide turbines, geothermal units, electrolyzers, fuel cells, hydrogen storage systems, etc. need to be built. Happily, the other half of the hydrogen-electricity infrastructure, the electricity grid, is already in place and paid for (in large part by government programs/incentives).

Chapter 5

Where Are We Now?

Before long, it will be as shortsighted (economically and environmentally) to burn hydrocarbons to produce electricity as it now is to produce light via incandescent lightbulbs. What was a good idea one hundred years ago (i.e., incandescent lightbulbs) reached a crossover point with compact fluorescents about ten years ago, and incandescents are now recognized as a very bad investment both economically and environmentally. Still, in American homes, the number of incandescents in use today dwarfs that of compact fluorescents. Humans tend to be slow to adopt good ideas, and this is one of the main roadblocks to alternative energy industries (e.g., wind, solar, geothermal).

You are probably wondering exactly where, economically speaking, the sources of alternative energy are relative to hydrocarbon-produced energy. Figure 5-1 depicts the decline in the cost of solar cells due largely to mass production. It plots the cost of a solar installation (close to $100,000 in 1976; about $3000 in 2000) against the total solar sales (in gigawatts) since 1976. The dramatic decline in the price of a solar installation, due to the efficiencies of mass production, is evident. This trend brings the cost of solar energy closer to the cost of grid-produced electricity.

It is important to note that our current grid electric rates (e.g., $.09 per kw hr) include the costs of their hydrocarbon sources of energy. Furthermore, since the cost of light is $0, it is the materials costs of solar cells that are now dramatically more expensive. However, this comparison is quite disingenuous in an important way. The cost of hydrocarbon-produced electricity that shows up on our utility bill includes none of the personal or societal costs (to our health, to the environment, to global climate change) that the industry produces. Our taxes cover these costs, so we are paying more for hydrocarbon-produced electricity than the bare $.09 per kw hr suggests. We also pay for hydrocarbon produced electricity via health insurance rates, hospital and medical costs, drug costs, home insurance rates, the property costs of hurricanes, flooding etc. Thus, the $.09 per kw hr is a very misleading figure. The real cost is at least two to three times the nominal cost. Conversely, *all* of the costs of solar energy are included in the values presented in Figure 5-1.

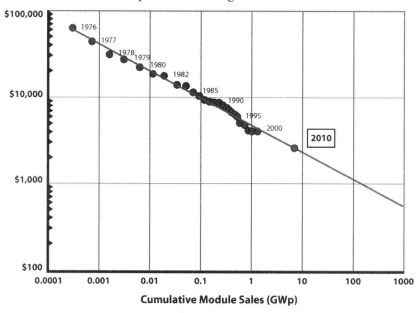

Figure 5-1.
Decline in cost of solar cells due largely to mass production.

Parenthetically, did you ever feel like crying out, "My taxes are too high!" or "My insurance and health care costs are too high!" Next time, make the more precise statement, "The environmental and health care costs of electricity generation should not be treated as externalities. I want a fair carbon tax!" [You'd be in good company, as 250 of our largest corporations recently called for a carbon tax.] What would happen? The cost of electricity would rise while our taxes and health care costs plummet. So would a carbon tax produce no net change? Absolutely not!

Figure 5-2 takes the decline in solar cost/cell from Figure 5-1 and compares it to the cost of grid hydrocarbon produced electricity over time. The broken line simply adds a $.03 carbon tax in 2007.

Without the carbon tax, the cost of grid electricity would equal solar electricity in about 2020. With the carbon tax, the crossover would have happened sometime in the 1990s. A carbon tax would make the use of grid electricity a lot like incandescent lightbulbs—economically irrational. So we'd all rush out to get solar cells for our roofs.

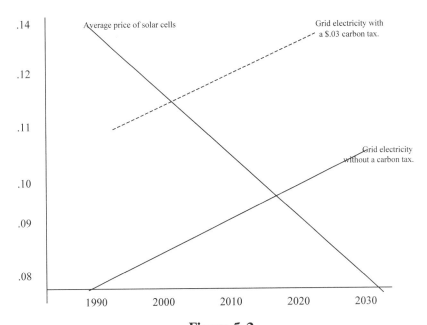

Figure 5-2.
Price of solar cells over time and the price of grid electricity
both with and without a green tax.

Whenever a carbon tax might be adopted, the original line in Figure 5-2 depicting the cost of grid-produced electricity would rise dramatically, and alternative energy products (e.g., solar, wind, geothermal) would instantly become more cost effective—thus accelerating their adoption. But there is more. Do you recall the current annual, tax free rate of return on your investment in a compact fluorescent lightbulb? 1150%! What does that become if the average cost of grid produced electricity is $.12 (with a carbon tax) rather than $.09? Try to figure that one out. The answer is in the last paragraph of this chapter.

No less an economic authority than Alan Greenspan (2007) made the comparable call for a carbon tax for transportation applications;

> We need significantly higher gasoline prices to wean us off gasoline-powered motor vehicles. The geopolitical price premium is apparently not large enough to do that unassisted. The expectation of higher gasoline prices through taxes (or an oil-supply squeeze) would galvanize large technical breakthroughs in the production of ethanol. Corn ethanol, though valuable, can play only a limited role, because its ability to displace gasoline is modest at best. One bushel of corn yields only 7.2 gallons of ethanol, which means that all 11 billion bushels of corn that the United States produced in 2006 would have yielded only 5.2 million barrels of ethanol a day, the energy equivalent of 3.9 million barrels a day of gasoline, or only a third of U.S. highway use, and less than a fifth of the 21 million barrels a day Americans consumed in 2006. And, of course, if all corn were devoted to ethanol, our pigs would starve. Cellulosic ethanol derived from switchgrass or agricultural waste seems to hold greater promise. A joint study by the U.S. Department of Agriculture and Department of Energy credibly estimates that fuels derived from plant matter, or biomass, have "the potential of sustainably supplying much more than one-third of the nation's current petroleum consumption." Other countries' use of biodiesel fuel, which is derived from vegetable oils and other sources, can add to the displacement of OPEC petroleum.
>
> Alternatively, if ethanol fails and if gasoline prices are high enough, plug-in hybrids will significantly displace petroleum consumption over time. Battery technology is making gradual progress; there is already ample electric power being generated to supply plug-

ins, particularly if power companies move more toward peak-load pricing. If we can shed our fear of nuclear power, the concern that plug-in hybrids will ultimately be powered from conventional electric utilities burning polluting coal will be resolved.

Conventional hybrid cars, cars running on cellulosic ethanol, and plug-ins could displace a major part of the petroleum burned on U.S. highways. Wider use of more efficient diesel engines could induce further significant displacement of petroleum. But to speed such displacement would require either a vast increase in supplies of cellulosic ethanol or very expensive gasoline. Taxes can ensure the latter. I consider the argument that gasoline tax hikes are politically infeasible irrelevant. Sometimes the duty of political leadership is to convince constituencies that they are just plain wrong. Leaders who do not do that are followers.

A gasoline tax would not impose a very large burden, especially if phased in over a number of years. U.S. household motor fuel outlays, at 3 percent of disposable income in early 2007, are where they were from 1953 to 1973 and far below the 4.5 percent experienced during the crisis of 1980. Even at heights of $3-plus per gallon in July 2006, motor fuel consumed only 3.8 percent of disposable personal income. Yet Americans are very sensitive to gasoline prices. We complain when they rise. Americans nonetheless continue to drive as much as before. In the face of gasoline price spikes, they reduce mileage driven only for a short while. The average number of miles driven per licensed driver has continued to drift upward from 10,500 miles per driver in 1980 to 14,800 miles in 2006, an increase of 1.3 percent per year. With higher prices, since 2002 the increase has slowed to 0.2 percent per year. Drivers consume less gasoline only because they eventually buy more fuel-efficient cars.

It should be obvious that as long as the United States is beholden to potentially unfriendly sources of oil and gas, we are vulnerable to economic crises over which we have little control. Petroleum is so embedded in today's economic world that an abrupt severance of supply could disrupt our economy and those of other countries. U.S. national security will eventually require that we see petroleum as an energy source of choice, not necessity.

Greenspan arrived at his conclusion after a thorough evaluation of our present energy situation. If only our country had the wisdom and leadership to follow Greenspan's sage advice.

When Does Solar Make Economic Sense

The energy contained in hydrocarbons originated from sunlight. Through a life, death, decay and chemical change process over many hundreds of thousands of years the energy comes to us as coal, oil, and natural gas. Photovoltaics and wind energy eliminate the "hundreds of thousands of years" intermediate steps. Photons of sunlight strike solar cells (photovoltaics) to produce electricity. Or by taking advantage of air movements produced by uneven heating of the earth's surface by the sun (wind), we also obtain electricity. As shown in Figure 5-2, costs of the devices required to convert sunlight to electricity are declining dramatically. However, there are other factors (i.e., incentives, amount of sunlight) that cut the difference between grid produced electricity and power produced via solar cells.

Since the start of the 21st Century, these factors originally favored Japan and Germany where most solar installations were sited. Later, countries such as Spain and Italy became attractive sites. In the United States, California led the way, soon to be followed by Arizona, New Mexico, New Jersey, Oregon and other states. The example below provides a quantification of these factors in a comparison of my state, Indiana, with California.

Location, Location, Location

This mantra of real estate agents also describes the current situation for the adoption of alternative energy devices. Imagine you are the C.E.O. of *Target* and need to decide whether *Wal-Mart* is making a good business decision in putting photovoltaic cells on the roofs of their stores. What factors might you consider?

First, there is a factor that works against the "location…" theme. The Federal Government gives a 30% (of all costs) tax credit (which is far more valuable than a tax deduction) to anyone who purchases alterative energy producing devices. While this credit is capped at $2000 for residential applications, it is unlimited (up to 30%) for commercial applications like *Target*. This factor favors no location in the U.S. over another. The 30% federal incentive is calculated after state incentives are deducted from the project's costs.

Now imagine you are thinking about a pilot project on stores in either Indianapolis, IN or Sacramento, CA. What factors should steer your choice of the pilot's location? Insolation, local electricity prices, and state incentive programs are the crucial variables. The table below presents values for these factors for an Indianapolis and a Sacramento location for a photovoltaic installation costing $352,000.

	Indianapolis	Sacramento
Federal Tax Credit	$90,000	$61,000
Insolation (Expressed in sales of KWH produced/year)	$4,176	$11,164
Cost of Grid Electricity ($/KWHr)	$5.88	$11.63
State Incentives	$0	$150,000
Sale of RECs	$1,080	$2,400
Full Payback of Investment (aided by accelerated depreciation)	123 years	6.4 years

The Sacramento installation would produce more electricity than the Indianapolis facility (insolation) that could replace more expensive grid produced electricity. The last factor to consider is state and local incentives. Governor Schwarzenegger's "Million Solar Roofs" program offers a return of 30% of the project's cost. California also has generous county, municipal, and utility company credits which differ significantly in various locales. Finally, because they have a vigorous REC (Renewable Energy Credits) program, a more attractive minimum price can be assigned for California RECs.

A few simplifying assumptions might be noted. The average cost of electricity in a state was used because of two offsetting factors: corporations get lower than average electricity rates, but all the electricity produced by solar is more expensive peak time electricity. Thus, these factors should cancel out one another. Similarly, the payback times include no cost for money which makes our estimate overly optimistic. However, 2005 electricity rates were used throughout. They are already overly conservative and likely to become more so with each passing year.

Complete payback for the system when sited in Sacramento is 6.4 years. When an identical system is sited in Indianapolis, payback time is 123 years. Thus, a California location is easily justified on business grounds compared to Indiana. For now, it's location, location, location. So good is the California proposition that many venture capital funds will gladly fund this initial project. The *Target* C.E.O. can put a solar roof on the facility without making any financial investment at all. Of course, the venture capital fund owns the installation, electricity, the federal, state, local, and utility incentives, the REC credits, etc. But by signing an electricity purchase agreement far into the future, *Target* insulates itself from the inevitable increases in utility rates that the future holds for us. Finally, the positive publicity that *Target* receives from installing solar panels is hard to quantify. We suspect the *Target* C.E.O. will choose wisely whether or not to own the facility, and we know *Target* will choose its location wisely.

The enormous difference in payback times is due to three factors. The first factor is the amount of state incentives: $150,000 in California, $0 in Indiana. You can see what incentives your state offers by going to *www.dsreusa.org* and clicking on your state in the map of the USA.

The second variable is called insolation—the amount of sunlight a part of the country typically receives. Figure 5-3 provides a rough view of insolation figures for various regions of the United States (higher numbers mean greater amounts of sunlight). More precise insolation figures for the amount of sunlight in your city can be obtained at *www.solarseller.com/solar_insolation_maps_and_chart_.htm*

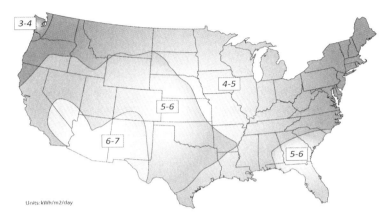

Figure 5-3. Insolation map of the United States.

The last factor to be considered in deciding the payback time in the siting of a solar installation is the cost of grid electricity in that location. Figure 5-4 presents the average price of grid electricity in each state for 2005.

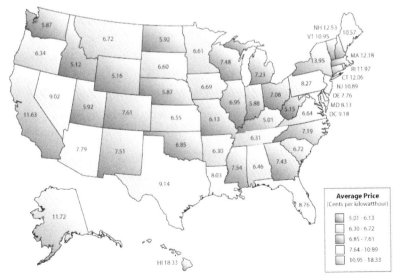

Figure 5-4. Average price of grid electricity in each state in 2005.

Finally, Figure 5-5 combines almost all of the information above in a graph of photovoltaic isocurves that plots insolation and electricity costs against the actual changing cost/watt of solar cells over time. Los Angeles, CA was the first large city where the cost of solar electricity became equal to grid produced electricity. That event occurred sometime late in 2004, when the cost/watt of solar cells was a shade over $6/watt. Given current insolation and cost of electricity figures, Seattle will still have cheaper grid electricity more than twenty years from now.

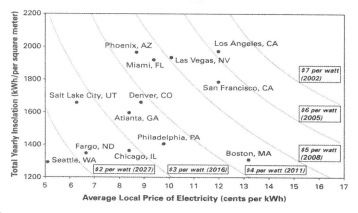

Figure 5-5. PV isocost curves for the United States at various cost levels of PV systems and how PV economics for various cities will change over time. *Source:* EIA (2005); NASA

How a Carbon Tax Would Speed Alternative Power Sources

Recall that many of the real costs of grid produced electricity have been externalized (as the economists say) and so the cost figures of electricity in Figure 5-4 are far too low to reflect the reality of our lives. An honest solution would be to add a carbon tax to the price of grid produced electricity to reflect its real cost to our society (Harden, 1993). Answer the following riddle, "How can we initiate new taxes, but pay no more in taxes?" An answer might be by initiating "green taxes" that will replace dollar-for-dollar our federal income taxes. First, what is a green tax, and why is it a business-friendly way to environmental sanity? The Box entitled "A Hard Working Tax" begins an explanation of green taxes.

A Hard Working Tax

Capitalizing upon your new knowledge of the finances of lightbulbs, imagine that a green tax of $.10 was levied on the sale of all incandescent lightbulbs (whether produced domestically or abroad). The cost is immediately passed on to the consumer, who would now pay $1.04 per bulb. Thus, *GE*'s profit for each bulb is unchanged. Consumers pay no more in total taxes because federal tax rates would be lowered to produce income tax savings that are equal to the total of all green taxes collected. Thus, a consumption tax replaces an income tax dollar-for-dollar to produce no net change in taxation. As with sales taxes, businesses collect green taxes, which moves the IRS a bit further from our lives. Paul Hacken claims that if we took green taxes seriously, we might put the IRS completely out of business. Wouldn't that be a pleasant, indirect outcome! The green tax on incandescent lightbulbs would rise to $.20 in the second year, $.30 in the third year, and so on until the twentieth year, when the final green tax level of $2 per bulb would arrive. By then, we would almost all be converted to compact fluorescents because, at over $2.94 per bulb, who would prefer incandescents to compact fluorescents? Lightbulb companies continue to earn the same profit, but now it comes from the sale of efficient technologies rather than wasteful technologies. The twenty year phase-in period enables all lightbulb companies the time to make whatever adjustments are necessary to adapt to the changing market conditions produced by the green tax. Everyone knows that our current income tax serves as a disincentive to earning, saving, and investing. If $10 billion were raised in green taxes on incandescent bulbs over a twenty year period, then $10 billion in disincentives would be removed from our income tax bills. However, there are known problems with all consumption taxes (e.g., they are regressive), and such problems will need to be worked out for any green taxes. But whereas other consumption taxes are crude—like saturation bombing—green taxes work with the precision of "smart" bombs. If we taxed all lightbulbs (presumably because they are involved in producing pollution), the supply-demand laws suggest that people would buy fewer lightbulbs—thereby cutting consumers' level of affluence (the A-term in I = PAT) and also reducing corporations' profits. In contrast, however, with a green tax on incandescents, consumers will (in the longer run) spend a smaller percentage of their income on lighting, while corporate profits from lightbulbs still go essentially unchanged.

Some industrial problems require an even finer-grained approach to green taxes. Instances where a good product/bad product distinction does not fit so easily require a more nuanced approach. For example, electric utilities use many energy sources to generate power (e.g., hydro, coal, natural gas, solar, oil). Rather than coarsely labeling some as "good" and others as "bad," a more precise tailoring of taxes would better serve our national interests. A panel of energy and environmental experts might rank-order the various fuel sources with respect to many factors (e.g., amount and type of pollutants; domestically available/imported; renewable/non-renewable), yielding the following relationships with respect to the undesirability of each fuel source:

Source undesirability:	Coal	=	Oil	>	Natural Gas	>	Hydro	>	Solar	=	Wind	=	Geothermal
Maximum green tax:	100%		100%		50%		25%		00%		00%		00%

The lower line indicates the percentage of some maximum level of green tax to be placed upon each energy source of electricity. Thus, the price of electricity produced by non-renewable, polluting, and imported fuel sources would increase dramatically. Conversely, renewable, non-polluting, domestic sources would pay no green tax. Again, such taxes might be phased in over twenty years, and the trillions of dollars raised would lead to enormous reductions in the amount of federal income taxes we pay. The problem of ozone depletion (caused by chlorofluorocarbons) might have been solved via green taxes rather than the phased-in bans that were employed. Similarly, the ratio of fuel efficient to fuel inefficient cars on our highways could also be increased via green tax solutions.

Free Markets: Reality or Fiction?

Do green taxes represent unwelcome intrusions into the actions of our free marketplace? Perhaps to the surprise of many readers, my answer is "Absolutely not!" Many writers (e.g., Harden, 1993; Hawken, 1993; Henderson, 1981) have argued that our present markets are not free and properly functioning precisely because all of the *real* costs of our goods and services are not included in their market prices. Green taxes would allow us to enter real costs (e.g., the price of emitting greenhouse gases; producing acid rain; depleting non-renewable resources; damaging people's health; destroying natural habitats) into market prices. The destructive consequences of our business practices are currently being treated as externalities. Green taxes allow us to internalize these externalities, and thus would produce (perhaps for the first time) a complete, truly-free market that might then be able to work its wonders.

The renewable, efficient, and non-polluting technologies that will dominate the 21st Century cannot compete in a marketplace that will not fairly charge inefficient, polluting, non-renewable competitors for their negative impacts. In the lightbulb example, because *GE*'s sales and profits continue to come from their more wasteful, polluting product (i.e., incandescent bulbs), *GE* is virtually mandated not to move more aggressively in pushing the efficient technologies that we need to solve our environmental crises.

During the 1992 Global Environmental Summit held in Rio de Janeiro, our Japanese and European competitors openly declared their belief that, "the development of energy efficient technologies represents the largest potential market in the history of the world." Because the prices of gasoline and electricity in Japan and Europe are far higher than they are in the United States (due to taxes that act like green taxes), American companies used to possess a slight, short-term competitive edge. But these same American companies now are crippled in their struggle to develop the technologies of efficiency because our energy costs are artificially low. I fear that the long-term competitiveness of American business is being sacrificed at the altar of a short-term competitive advantage. In my opinion, this is the central reason why American automobile companies have been so soundly thrashed by their Asian competitors in the race to supply hybrid electric automobiles.

Our low cost of energy also stimulates greater overall energy consumption. Is it any wonder that we, as Americans, are responsible for 26% of the world's energy consumption (United Nations, 1998) —even though we have less than 10% of the world's population? Green taxes would be an excellent first step toward rectifying our overreliance on cheap energy. Such taxes would immediately make clean, renewable, energy-efficient, alternative technologies more cost-effective. The prospect of gradually increasing green taxes on non-renewable, polluting hydrocarbons over the next two decades will enable American businesses to pursue the technologies of efficiency more aggressively, as we quickly phase-out the inefficient, polluting technologies of the 20th Century. Figure 5-2 shows the decline in price of solar cells over time. It also depicts how the addition of a green tax of $.03/kw hr would make solar cells competitive with grid electricity much more quickly. Finally, as business collects more and more green tax revenues, we will approach that glorious day when we might say, "Remember the bad old days, when we used to have to pay income taxes..."

In Conclusion

Once sufficient amounts of solar cells are installed upon American roofs (a task requiring several decades) we will have sufficient amounts of clean, renewable electricity to perform any required task. Instead of heating our offices, factories, and homes by burning natural gas, we can heat them electrically (ideally, with the assistance of geothermal energy). Instead of fueling our transportation systems by burning gasoline, diesel, and the like, all vehicles could be powered electrically. Larger, more efficient propulsion batteries would be required, of course. However, the propulsion battery industry is now experiencing geometric growth as companies like *Cobasys* [nickel-metal hydride (NiMH) and lithium ion (Li-I)], *Matsushita* [NiMH & Li-I], *Johnson Controls* [NiMH & Li-I], *A-123* [Li-I], and *Altair Nanotechnologies* [Li-I] beautifully demonstrate.

Of course, one can obtain enormous amounts of electricity from various sources (i.e., wind, geothermal, hydro, nuclear, tides) without burning hydrocarbons, so the complete burden for producing electricity does not fall upon solar. However, a recent analysis of the capacity of several completely clean approaches demonstrates that solar compares very favorably to the other approaches, and thus will likely be the workhorse of the 21st Century's energy systems. See Table 5-1.

Table 5-1.

Maximum Output for Alternative Energy Sources

To maintain CO_2 levels at or below 550ppm, by the year 2050 the world will need 17TW of new carbon-free energy, and 33TW by 2100

Potential sources of carbon-free energy, and the amount of energy that each could contribute, are:

• Wind	2 – 4	TW
• Tidal	2	TW
• Hydro	1.6	TW
• Bio Fuels	5 – 7	TW
• Geothermal	2 – 4	TW
• Solar	*600*	TW

- Solar PV is viewed to be *the* solution to fill the 17TW energy gap
- ~10TW must include some form of storage—hydrogen provides the energy storage solution
- Solar Hydrogen economy is the ultimate carbon-free energy solution

Source: Argonne National Labs/Cal Tech

Finally, adding a $.03 green tax to our $.09/kw hr electricity rate raises the annual rate of return on our additional investment in buying compact fluorescents from 1150% to 1380%. That is, each year you use the compact fluorescent bulb, your original additional investment is returned to you almost fourteen times over.

Chapter 6

The Greening of Business

This chapter will provide an example that presents several issues to be considered by any company looking to implement a program to move into solar energy sources. Let's say a large U.S. corporation contacted *Inovateus Development* (a distributor of photovoltaic cells) early in 2007 to expand their environmental efforts into clean energy technologies. Historically, the Company had made major environmental contributions through its more efficient burning of hydrocarbons (cogeneration) and water desalination and purification systems. In 2007, the Company's leadership saw the need to generate ever increasing amounts of clean and renewable electricity for the future through solar power.

Site Analysis

Nine months were spent planning with the Company's Global Alternative Energy Purchasing Director. During this time, multiple potential sites in the U.S. and Europe were identified and an alliance with a company (*1 Star Energy*) to install photovoltaic cells and warranty their performance was forged. Because site managers were crucial players in investment decisions at the Company, some excellent sites were by-passed while a few marginal (because of limited state incentives) sites were considered.

Next, analyses of various potential sites were then developed. Table 6-1 specifies the characteristics of a few projects. Only projects where *UNI-SOLAR* thin film photovoltaic cells were proposed are included in Table 6-1 to ensure the comparability of data across sites. As noted in Chapter 5, the differences in the size of the solar installations in Table 6-1 relate to roof area, incentives, and the pricing strategies of local utilities. Differences in incentives generally relate to the amount of help that each state or nation offers. Payback time and internal rate of return are also sensitive to local utility rates and the amount of sunlight received in each location. European nations do not offer incentives, but rather help with Feed in Tariffs (FIT). FITs work by having governments purchase electricity for a long time period (e.g., 25 yrs.) at a very high price (e.g., $.80/kw hr) to incentivize adoption of solar power. As you can see in Table 6-1, the Company's options for consideration were diverse on these dimensions.

Table 6-1

Example of a Site Comparison made for the Company

	Installation Size	Cost	Incentives	Payback	Internal Rate of Return
Illinois	500kw	$3.17M	$0.96M	15 yrs	9.2%
California	250kw	$1.62M	$1.02M	9 yrs	16.9%
Ohio	250kw	$1.68M	$0.65M	11 yrs	13.3%
Oregon	612kw	$3.98M	$1.65M	3 yrs	25%
Arizona	250kw	$1.68M	$1.01M	5 yrs	21.6%
Germany	500kw	$3.17M	$ 0	10 yrs	FIT=$0.49@kw hr
Spain	500kw	$3.17M	$ 0	9 yrs	FIT=Complex

The Box below, entitled "After Further Review," outlines the problems of comparing Payback times when different types of incentives are employed, and illustrates the importance of identifying and weighing the factors which are relevant to a company's unique situation.

After Further Review

Payback time is usually the best measure of an investment's value to a company. While working with a top 25 company of the Fortune 500 list, I noticed that by installing solar cells in Phoenix, Arizona, in 2007, the payback time was five years. The same system, if sited in Germany, would be paid back in ten years. Thus, the Arizona installation makes better business sense. Right?

In the National Football League, every play is called on the field (analogously, the payback time). However, a coach can challenge calls made on the field, and a review by the referee of videotapes of the play determines whether the play stands as called on the field, or whether the official's original call is reversed. The report of such reviews begins with the words, "After further review…"

Germany's 10-year payback would be inferior to Arizona's 5-year payback if the incentives each site receives are of the same type. In this case they are not. So let's review the original call: that a 5-year payback beats a 10-year payback. The cost of the solar installation (250 kw) in Arizona and Germany is roughly equal ($1,687,284.).

Arizona gives $1,031,185, in Federal and State incentives, so the company really has $656,099 invested in the solar project. Because this company only pays $.047 per kw hr for its electricity, the company saves $19,364 in electricity costs in the first year of the installation's service life. [Other tax breaks are needed to achieve the 5-year payback. Payback would be in about 32 years if the $656,099 needed to be paid back solely by electricity savings at about $20,000 per year.] So after about five years, the company has its investment returned and receives about $20,000 per year in electricity benefits (assuming electricity rates remain unchanged).

In Germany, solar is incentivized in a different manner. Unlike the United States, Germany offers no incentives to buy down the cost of the company's investment. Thus, the company invests $1,687,284 in the solar installation. Because they get less sunlight than Arizona, the German installation gets only about 75% of the electricity that Arizona generates, but the government pays $.49 per kw hr for the electricity. This values the electricity at over 10-times the valuation of the Arizona electricity. Thus, the solar installation produces more than $150,000 worth of electricity each year in Germany.

At year 10, the Arizona facility has returned a $100,000 profit while the German project has just broken even. Looks like Arizona wins! At year 20, Arizona has a profit of $300,000 while Germany's profit is $1,500,000. This looks like a clear win for Germany, but it is actually a closer call than you might think. It took Germany ten years to retrieve its $1,687,284 investment, but Arizona only required five years to retrieve its $656,099 investment. Depending on the value you assign to money, Germany's $1,500,000 profit actually might be close to Arizona's $300,000 profit at this stage. At year 30, however, Germany's $3,000,000 profit clearly exceeds Arizona's $500,000 profit.

So which is the better business deal? Arizona's 5-year payback, if your businesses' time horizon is only ten years ($10,000 profit for Arizona, $0 for Germany). But Germany's 10-year payback time is far superior to Arizona's 5-year payback time if your time horizon is thirty years (Arizona's profit is $500,000, Germany's profit is $3,000,000). After further review, Germany wins—at least in my book.

It's important to note that changes in incentives, etc. are occurring constantly. For example, during 2007, Arizona, Illinois, Oregon and other states (as well as Spain and Italy in Europe) significantly enhanced their incentive programs.

Type of Solar Cell

Another decision to be made involves selecting the type of solar cell for the potential site. Crystalline solar cells are more efficient; but you want to buy *electricity*, not *efficiency*. A naïve understanding of efficiency would suggest that the more efficient cell would be best. However, the precise conditions that determine a cell's efficiency almost never occur in real life outside the lab. The more efficient crystalline cells have large performance drop-offs as real life conditions vary from the lab conditions. *UNI-SOLAR'*S thin film cells show small losses in the wide variety of real-world conditions (cloudy days, low light conditions, etc.). A detailed explanation regarding this comparison can be found in the Box below. It is the answer to one of the "Frequently Asked Questions" located on *Inovateus Development's* website.

Efficiency or Electricity?

"What is this *UNI-SOLAR* 15-20% power output advantage I keep hearing about?"

The *UNI-SOLAR* PV cell is especially good at collecting energy at low light levels. We were the original calculator solar cell back in the 1980s. It has been demonstrated at *TISO Labs* in Europe that the *UNI-SOLAR* PV cell is as much as 40% more efficient than all competitors when light levels are less than ¼ suns. This inherent ability to produce energy under low light levels is demonstrated as *UNI-SOLAR* PV arrays activate (turn on) line-tie inverters earlier in the morning than any other type of solar array. This results in more power into your AC Service Panel every year (per installed watt).

The visible spectrum of light that comes from the sun is familiar to us as the range of colors we see in a rainbow. The *UNI-SOLAR* amorphous silicon solar cell is especially good at collecting the blue part of the visible spectrum. The blue part of the rainbow is dominant in cloudy weather and it is dominant in summer weather. Since the summer is longer than winter in the U.S., Europe, most of China and all of India, Africa and

South America, the *UNI-SOLAR* PV array will be exposed to a favorable spectrum of light for more days of the year than, for example, crystalline cells that work especially well when the spectrum is skewed toward the red. We see a solar spectrum skewed to the red in Northern States and in Northern Europe during cold, clear days in the winter. Greater amounts of time under a favorable spectrum of light will result in more power into your AC Service Panel every year (per installed watt).

Take a close look at the data sheets for all *UNI-SOLAR* PV modules and you will notice the company quantifies the initial degradation that our PV modules experience upon their first few weeks of exposure to sunlight. Most other modules manufacturers do not quantify this initial degradation. For example, it has been shown that crystalline modules degrade – 2% from their rated power after initial exposure to sunlight. Since *UNI-SOLAR* modules have a greater (but predictable) degree of initial degradation, the company is very conservative in their module ratings. Recognition and quantification of this well-known phenomenon gives our customers more confidence that their *UNI-SOLAR* array will perform at its rated power.

UNI-SOLAR PV cells are interconnected with a bypass diode across EVERY solar cell. You can think of a *UNI-SOLAR* PV module in the same way you think about a 3-wire Christmas Tree Light string. If one bulb goes out, the rest stay lit. Same thing with a *UNI-SOLAR* module. If one of the cells is covered or shaded, or is damaged by flying debris during severe weather, the cell will be bypassed and the rest of the module will perform normally. This can be contrasted with most crystalline modules where there are only two bypass diodes in the J-box. Shade one cell and 50% of the module's power output is lost.

The *UNI-SOLAR* PV cells are protected by a "high-tech" plastic called ETFE. This plastic is a derivative of Teflon and allows typical rainfall to wash the modules clean. This plastic is also less reflective than the glass that protects crystalline solar cells. This less-reflective surface allows PV system owners to tilt their PV modules over a greater variety of tilt angles without suffering measurable losses. This effect has been documented at a site in Santa Cruz, California (*www.rmeter.com*, Electroroof Pilot) where *UNI-SOLAR* PV arrays laid flat on the deck are generating as much energy as polycrystalline modules mounted at an ideal tilt angle. Additionally, *UNI-SOLAR* is taking orders from airports across the U.S. that prefer *UNI-SOLAR* PV modules over the more reflective crystalline products. This attests to the low-glare surface of the *UNI-SOLAR* product.

So what is the "15-20% *UNI-SOLAR* power output advantage" you have been hearing about? It's all about:

1. The best low light response of any solar cell on the market,

2. A solar cell that responds well to the solar spectrum (sunlight) we see in the late Spring, Summer and Fall,

3. The lowest voltage drop (due to high temperature operation) compared to all other PV technologies,

4. A "thermal annealing" affect under high temperature operating conditions that increases current (amp) flow,

5. A recognition of the initial degradation of our PV modules and a conservative power rating that favors our customers,

6. Bypass diodes across every solar cell resulting in less power loss under shaded conditions,

7. Less-reflective top surface allowing for greater energy collection when the module is not oriented perpendicularly to the sun, and

8. Constant improvement to our terrestrial products driven by our advances in space cell development.

When the Company's Global Alternative Energy Purchasing Director raised the question regarding differences in efficiencies, I suggested the following thought experiments to better illustrate the complexities of comparing ratings.

Imagine your neighbor bought the exact same car that you did, except that his car had a six cylinder engine while your car had four cylinders. The neighbor delighted at pulling next to you at the red traffic light and challenging you to a race. You always lost badly. Knowing your car was rated at 38 mpg by the EPA and his was rated at 32 mpg, you challenged him to another contest. Both cars were to make the same 380-mile trip and you bet you'd get better gas mileage. Imagine your confidence when your neighbor required 10 gallons of gas (for a 32 mpg rate) to refill his car at the end of the trip. Imagine your horror when you required 10.2 gallons of gas (for a 31.8 mpg rate) to refill your car. "That's impossible!" you rage, "What went wrong with my car?"

The point here is that people tend to believe that different driving conditions affect all autos (and their EPA estimates) in similar ways, and that is indeed the case. Conversely, however, the performance ratings of photovoltaic cells will in fact become quite misleading as climate conditions (e.g., cloudy weather, very hot days, shade conditions) become less than optimal. Thus, unlike EPA ratings (which are expected to hold up well over a variety of driving conditions), performance ratings for solar cells do not predict very well the actual performance of solar cells for the range of real world light conditions.

Turning closer to home to apply what you learned from the previous thought experiment, now imagine you are the head of alternative energy at a multinational corporation. You own two buildings, (a factory and a distribution center) with equal roof size across the street from one another in Phoenix, Arizona. Two solar companies bid for contracts on the buildings. A crystalline photovoltaic company offers to put a 600 kw array on the roof for $3 million. A thin film photovoltaic company offers to put a 500 kw array on the roof (because amorphous thin film cells require more space per watt) for $3 million also. The thin film representative shows you three studies that suggest that amorphous thin film cells generate 15% more electricity per rated watt than crystalline cells in sunny conditions. Thus, you see the two offers as equal.

You tell the building managers to take their pick of the two offers. The factory manager is dubious of the research, so he chooses the crystalline cells for his roof. The distribution center's manager is concerned that the crystalline cells weigh many times what the amorphous thin film cells weigh, so he chooses the lighter amorphous cells. A year later, the two managers report that they generated almost exactly the same amount of energy, which was also almost exactly the amount that had been predicted (i.e., 15% more electricity per rated watt for amorphous thin film). Everyone was very pleased, and even more so because the Federal Government and the State of Arizona give generous incentives. In this case, your assumption that the two offers were equal was correct.

Word gets around in your corporation, and soon numerous other plant managers ask to be included in this alternative energy program. Flushed with your success, you offer all corporate locations the same deal ($3 million for 600 kw crystalline or $3 million for 500 kw amorphous thin film). You have assumed that the results obtained in Phoenix would travel well (i.e., generalize to other dissimilar locations). What is wrong with that assumption on your part? Let's take a look.

Three months after installation, the roof of a distribution plant in Minneapolis collapsed under the weight of the crystalline cells and a 24-inch snowfall. Because it doesn't snow in Phoenix, the weight difference (i.e., crystalline cells weigh about eight times more than amorphous cells) wasn't a real factor there.

A month later, one plant in South Bend reported that 80% of their crystalline cells had broken in a severe hail storm (i.e., glass laid horizontally on a roof is in grave danger in a hail storm). Another plant across town in South Bend had no hail damage; they had installed an amorphous thin film roof, which is virtually indestructible. (It doesn't hail in Phoenix either.)

So much for assuming generalizability to dissimilar climate locations. When you read an article that presents data suggesting that amorphous thin film cells obtain 20% or more electricity than crystalline cells in cloudy conditions (as opposed to their 15% superiority in always-sunny Phoenix), you think of a factory that is located in a city that often has cloudy weather. You suspect the crystalline cells will not fare as well in cloudy conditions, because you now know it's only safe to generalize results to similar climate conditions.

Potential Investments

An important charge to all business executives is to envision their business' future and to position their company to be ready for (or even to profit from) changed business environments. Because the Company had been profitable for close to seventeen decades, it already had an active investment program.

Any new business requires two important assets: (1) capital to develop products and to build production facilities and (2) markets for their products. While alternative energy companies have grown quickly of late, more assistance is required. There is still a great need for new sources of capital to fuel this expansion of production capacities. Sometimes investments serve as a win-win arrangement between the future needs of an established company and the current needs of a new business. For example, a handful of years earlier, the Company had made a significant investment in a lithium battery start-up company called *A-123*. At the time it was clear that lithium battery chemistries would take a bite out of the market for nickel-metal hydride batteries that had been established earlier by Stan Ovshinsky and *Energy Conversion Devices* in consumer products such as electric shavers, cell phones, IPODs, etc. Propulsion batteries for electric powered autos required the enhanced power and reduced weight that lithium batteries offered relative to the NiMH batteries (which continue to dominate the hybrid electric propulsion market). The company's investment in *A-123* helped with *A-123*'s capital needs at the time of the investment. The Energy Act of 2007 has virtually assured *A-123* access to enormous emerging markets for auto propulsion batteries through its provision that fleets of auto companies average 35 miles per gallon by 2020. The Company's investment in *A-123* clearly illustrates a win-win situation.

The Company has a division that is successful at selling consumer batteries, and possesses enormous resources in the manufacturing of batteries. *Energy Conversion Devices* has an alkaline fuel cell which resembles a battery. The fuel cell (unlike a tradition battery) can recharge by accepting hydrogen while it produces electricity. Thus, the two companies are discussing ways in which they can share their strengths in producing this hybrid battery-like fuel cell. Yet another win-win opportunity?

Chapter 7

The Heart of Free Markets:
Individual Consumers and Investors

To a clergyman, greed is a vice; to a psychologist, greed is an important part of human nature; to a denizen of Wall Street, greed is good. This chapter does not deal with greed in businesses. It points the finger in the other direction. What about greed in us?

Greed is historically considered a vice; while ambition is generally thought to be a virtue. However, both traits actually have a quirky constitution, and probably span the middle ground between virtues and vices. If asked what one thinks of greed and ambition, the answer might best begin with, "It depends on…"

First, greed in me. I've been a stockholder in *Energy Conversion Devices* for about seventeen years. The current (July 25, 2007) *ECD* stock price is a few dollars below my average "in price." Does that mean that I am furious or devastated because my greed has been thwarted? My answer is, "Not at all." On what does this answer depend in my, "It depends on…" answer?

Overall, my investments are doing reasonably well. We'll have a decent retirement; my children will be able to graduate from college free of debt; we are able to help relatives when necessary; and the like. Still, some of my money-making (and money-losing also) investments do not make me proud. Is one proud to have made money on companies that make cigarettes, alcohol, asbestos, and the like? Am I vexed to be losing money on a company like *Energy Conversion Devices*? The answer would be "yes" if for me money were an *end*, rather than a *means* to other, more important, ends.

Were I not doing decently overall, I might be unable to view my *ECD* "paper losses" so benignly. However, if I were unable to help a friend in financial need, I would love to be able to say, "Sorry, but I lost my money trying to help *Energy Conversion Devices*—a company struggling mightily to make the world a better place for our children." Often when I place an order with my broker (and friend) to "average down" my *ECD* position, he chastises me about "over-committing to a losing proposition" or "throwing good money after bad." I simply quote Dickens, "It is a far, far better thing that I do, than I have ever done; it is a far, far better rest that I go to than I have ever known" (*A tale of two cities*, closing lines). Do I hope that in time that sentiment becomes more true? Yes, with all my heart and soul. However, I hope even more that *ECD* succeeds. In fact, I hope that most alternative energy companies succeed—especially the five other alternative energy companies in which I also hold stock.

The Proper Use of Greed

Wherever you cast forth your money—your heart and mind will follow. I learned this simple truth in the course of thirty years of investing. Twenty years ago, a relative suggested a biotechnology stock I might buy. My interest in (and knowledge of) biotechnology at that time was close to zero. But the company seemed to have enormous potential and so my healthy lust for profit (if indeed greed is healthy as well as good) enticed me to invest. Two decades later, my promising biotech company stock sells for $1.14/share—a tiny fraction of the price I paid. That's okay, you pay your dues and you take your chances. It's all part of the investment game.

The more remarkable occurrence (than losing my money) is that I now know far more about the world of biotechnology than almost anyone who is not professionally employed in the biotech world. That is a remarkable outcome given my profound initial ignorance of (and complete lack of interest in) biotechnology. Because my money followed a "biotech tip," I gradually became a biotech person. In 1990, I was 100% invested in biotechnology stocks—when I bought my first shares of *ECD*. Today I am 97% invested in alternative energy stocks.[3]

---

[3] Before all my financial analyst readers die in abject horror at my investment strategies, let me say that *all* of my Notre Dame retirement money is tied up in boring, CREF bonds. Even if the alternative energy markets implode completely, my retirement will still be fine. Were I interested in minimizing risk I'd behave differently. Instead my goal is to focus my attention on environmental issues—and hope I earn a reasonable rate of return on alternative energy stocks.

My first purchase of *ECD* stock introduced me to the world of alternative energy. I believe that initial investment acted like a grappling hook that I used to remake myself and my interests. This is my fourth book that discusses alternative energy—how many other psychologists have done that? I'm suggesting that if more of my colleagues were invested in alternative energy stocks, I wouldn't be nearly as lonely as an environmental psychologist.

Charitable giving has long been recognized as a way to *project* one's values into the future. Rarely do we think of our investments as a step toward *creating* the type of future we would like to see emerge. However, since ready access to sources of capital remains a challenge for most developmental stage companies, any investment in a company's stock somewhat strengthens its financial position. From that perspective, one would need to be cautious about investments in tobacco companies, makers of distilled spirits, casino stocks, and the like. Of course, if one viewed investing only as a way to make money, then other values would merely be a nuisance.

You Are What You Eat

The media has noted that the incidence of childhood obesity has tripled over the last three decades. What is the reason for this alarming health trend? Again, the media asserts that the amount of "fast food" in childrens' diets is a primary cause. However, we are consumers in many ways other than what we eat.

Each of us has a "carbon footprint." This is the amount of carbon dioxide that each of us generates through our daily activities. Most of our carbon footprint is caused by our consumption of energy. Whether you warm your home with natural gas, or play video games using electricity produced by burning coal, or drive to work in a gasoline powered automobile, each of these activities (and many others also) adds to the size of your carbon footprint.

I recently shrunk the size of my carbon footprint. I traded my station wagon (a gas guzzling beast if there ever was one) for a *Prius*. Tripling the gas mileage of my car cuts the transportation portion of my carbon footprint by two-thirds. How big an improvement is that? Well, suppose I offered to cut your monthly rent or mortgage by two-thirds. Instead of a monthly mortgage payment of $1164, I'd only pay $388. Anyone interested in that deal? Well, the earth and its ecosystems are equally interested in both of us reducing our carbon footprint by two-thirds.

Recall that, in Chapter 3, we advocated replacing 100w incandescent bulbs with 28w compact florescent bulbs (they produce about the same light). The earth would love that 74% reduction in the lighting portion of your carbon footprint. Similarly, replacing my natural gas furnace with a geothermal unit reduced the heating and cooling portion of my carbon footprint by over 90%.

I'm now ready to tie together these rambling thoughts on consumption and investing. Earlier we noted how the sale of compact fluorescent lightbulbs went from a tiny trickle ten years ago to a raging torrent today. As these economies of scale kicked-in, the price of a compact fluorescent bulb plummeted from $20 to $2.53 currently. In 1997, I had forty compact fluorescents in my home. Each bulb was working hard (at earning 57% return on investment per year, tax free) to cut my monthly electric bill (Howard, 1997, p. 99). Here is the key move in my plan to adopt a "strategic voluntary simplicity" in my life. Instead of using my electricity savings to consume *more* (e.g., eat out once more each week; go out to movies; buy a bigger, newer car), I return the savings to an account that I use to *further our energy future*.

Some of this pool of savings was invested in enhancing my energy efficiency. I now have more than sixty compact fluorescents in my home; I bought a geothermal heating and cooling unit for my home; I now drive a hybrid electric automobile; and I soon hope to install photovoltaic cells on my roof. Not only do these investments save electricity (that my utility produces largely [about 95%] by burning coal), but they also save more money, which I add to my alternative energy account.

Early on, I realized there simply were not enough energy saving home uses for this pool of saved money. So I bought stocks in a range of alternative energy companies with the surplus cash. This strategy allowed me to do my part to make alternative energy companies successful. By purchasing energy saving devices, I increased the market for these companies' new products. By purchasing stocks in the alternative energy companies, I increased their ability to fund their research and development efforts, because floating new shares is the most common way for money-losing companies to fund their activities. Thus, I have aided these companies' need for additional capital.

The astute reader will recognize that a parallel program of purchasing energy saving equipment and reinvesting profits into the purchase of more energy saving products was described in Chapter 6 for a large company. By investing in this manner, both individuals and businesses further ensure their economic future while they dramatically diminish the strain they put on the earth and its ecosystems by reducing the size of their carbon footprint. I believe each of us (as individuals and as businesses) should initiate a small program of decreasing our energy consumption and reinvesting the profits into subsequent rounds of alternative energy purchases. Before long you will be repeating the words of the late senator from Illinois, Everett Dirkson, "A million here, a million there. Pretty soon you're talking real money." Or as an environmentalist might observe: A kilowatt here, a kilowatt there. Pretty soon you're talking real progress.

In this manner, we harness your and my greed in order to make money for the alternative energy companies' struggle to produce solutions to our environmental problems. I cannot think of a better use for the "virtue" greed.

Chapter 8

Our Collective Vision: Politics

Long ago, I asked my uncle, "What is politics all about?"

"It's all about who's ox is being gored," he replied wryly.

The older I get, the more truth I find in his answer. As soon as people decide to become a group (e.g., a family, a clan, a city-state, a corporation, a country, a member of the United Nations) it becomes apparent that some tasks are best undertaken collectively (e.g., protection from criminals, national defense, the provision of utilities like electricity, trash removal, water, etc.). Politics can be seen as the process whereby we choose how to provide those collective goods, and who will pay the bill.

About a century ago, our political representatives realized that affordable electricity would need to be provided for virtually all citizens. A key developmental challenge was the building of the enormous infrastructure (the electricity grid) required to offer electricity to citizens. If this challenge was left to free enterprise, multiple companies would each erect their own infrastructures and then compete for your electricity business. The waste involved in having *multiple* electricity infrastructures in one area led our legislatures to award the ownership of electricity production and distribution in an area to *one* company, which became your local electric utility. Because of the lack of competition fostered by this system, each state set up a board (and a set of procedures) to oversee electricity rates and, from time to time, to approve rate increases.

Americans received low cost electricity for many years because of this arrangement. However, in the last two decades of the 20th Century, this "captured markets served by one electric utility" approach was modified somewhat. There evolved some degree of competitive markets wherein multiple utilities could bid to supply electricity to businesses and/or residences in another company's area. This free competition approach was, at best, only modestly successful. Currently, the overwhelming majority of people still get their electricity from their local utility.

The cost structure of each utility included the cost of generation facilities (i.e., power plants), personnel costs, fuel costs (i.e., coal, oil, natural gas), the repair and upkeep of each utility's local portion of the grid, and other miscellaneous costs. All utilities are about equally subject to most of these aspects of the company's cost structure. However, upkeep of one's portion of the grid is a cost born by the local utility, but not a cost for its potential competitors in the local grid's area. When the choices are to give your competitors an advantage or to ignore maintenance and repair of your portion of the grid, most companies seriously underinvest in the upkeep of their portion of the grid. Thus, our national electricity grid is in a state of disrepair, as seen by the incidence of breakdowns, brownouts, and blackouts. Should our Federal Government step in and rescue the grid? That is a very difficult question to answer. As you think about issues of taxation, government funding of some businesses but not others, and the role of political leadership, perhaps a thought experiment will clear the intellectual underbrush enough to enable us to venture an answer.

A Thought Experiment

You are the Speaker of the U.S. House of Representatives. [No need to thank me for giving you that juicy role.] The year is 1915. Henry Ford has just led you and three other guests on a tour of his brand new River Rouge assembly plant. Now the five of you sit down for lunch. Thaddeus Horsehide, owner of the world's largest Buggy Whip conglomerate opens by saying, "Mr. Speaker, the buggy whip industry pays more in taxes each year than the automobile and airplane industries have paid in their entire history." Wilbur and Orville Wright (nearly choking on their potato skins) object by saying their industry has not yet begun, and that in time they and automakers would pay many more dollars in taxes than buggy whip manufacturers. Ford likes the Wright Brothers' answer and adds, "Everyone knows government funding is intended to seed the industries of the future, not to further reward the winners of the past." Mr. Horsehide grumbles about paying too much in taxes, but he knows that horse drawn buggies are the transportation of the past—not the future. You end this part of the conversation by asserting that public funds need to be used where they will assist American companies to become central players in the technologies of the future.

Henry Ford notes that his factory is mass producing autos right now, and that the amount of taxes the auto industry will pay in the next two to three decades will be enormous. The Wright Brothers see flight as an important industry also, even though it might not develop as quickly as the auto industry.

But because you are a member of House Armed Services Committee, your thoughts roam beyond consideration of taxes. "The winds of war are blowing in Europe," you observe. "Which technology will help us most if we go to war?"

"The cavalry has always been an essential part of any army's..." Thaddeus Horsehide began expansively.

"Not in the coming war," Henry Ford cuts in. "Tanks and other mechanized vehicles will rule the battlefield."

"And airplanes also," Wilbur added.

"Not in this war," Henry Ford repeats.

"Yes, some planes will play a role in this war," Orville breaks in, "even if it's a minor role. But, God forbid, what if there's a second world war?"

This last comment leads you to doubt a conclusion that was forming in your mind. It was clear that Thaddeus Horsehide would get no government money. Henry Ford would get lots of government money. But should he get it all?

And so the thought experiment ends. But you, careful reader, and I are in a privileged position. Having witnessed the way in which the 20th Century played itself out, we know the way you should have allocated the government's scarce resources back in 1915, don't we? Seventy-five percent should have gone to Ford, twenty-five percent to the Wright Brothers, nothing to Mr. Horsehide. Of course, no one is pleased with this "Truth." Henry wanted 90% of the money, with the Wrights getting 10%. The Wrights wanted 75%, with Henry getting 25%. And Thaddeus wanted something back, given all the taxes he has paid over the years. What division of the tax dollars do you think would have been wise?

What actually occurred? Well, that's a difficult question to answer, but I think it's fair to say that Ford's "oxen" and the Wright Brothers' "oxen" were appropriately fattened at the public feed trough during the 20th Century. I'm unaware of any buggy whip factories funded by our government during the last century. Thaddeus' bovines were savaged.

Oddly enough, the previous thought experiment positions us to determine how well our government performed in passing the nightmarish Energy Act of 2005 and the only slightly better Energy Act of 2007. Now we have a different cast of characters. Thaddeus Horsehide no longer represents the technologies of the past and present; he's replaced by Mr. Exxon (oil, natural gas) and Mr. Ashland (coal). Representing the near future is Mr. Corn Ethanol, rather than Henry Ford. Mr. Solar and Mr. Wind have the best long term prospects as workhorse energy sources, as did the Wright Brothers.

You can construct the justification for each industry getting the lion's share of new federal monies any way you wish. We now know that over 90% of the new monies in the 2005 energy bill went to the industries of the past (i.e., oil, coal, natural gas, nuclear), while less than 10% went to the clean and renewable energy technologies of the future (i.e., solar, wind, geothermal, biofuels, tides). One can only wonder how wise that political decision will look to denizens of the latter half of the 21st Century. But this is no time for sulking. Because your allocation of resources in 1915 proved Solomonian, you were promoted to the position of the Secretary of Energy.

Perhaps a new day is dawning. After all, the Democrats (who are generally more positive on forward looking energy policies) regained control of both houses of Congress in 2006. This Congress tried to remove $14 billion in incentives for hydrocarbon industries from the Energy Act of 2005 and vowed to give it to the clean and renewable alternative energy industries in the 2007 energy bill. How promising would that move have been? Furthermore, now the 2008 election looms, and prospects for pro-environment candidates look bright. Perhaps we can now reverse all of the 2005 trends in oxen-abuse. Ah, if wishing could make it so.

When Hitler threatened Americans and their liberty, I, for one, was thrilled that we had plentiful tanks and warplanes to repel the German and Japanese threats. I just don't think a cavalry charge would have carried the day. Who knows the ways our energy system will be threatened in the future? However, I'd like our chances a whole lot more if our system was clean, renewable, and distributed (i.e., not made in centralized power plants). Can we ever elect enough politicians who support alternative energy initiatives? Given that the Energy Bill of 2007 was gutted in the eleventh hour of a Renewable Energy Standard, help for solar and wind power, etc., it appears that our political will is still insufficient. Our recent trends in government funding (circa 2000-2007) are quite troubling. They call to mind an ancient warning from the *I Ching*: "One who spends too much time living in the past has no future."

Tying Up Some Loose Ends

Two decades ago we couldn't decide whether ozone depletion or global warming was the worse environmental threat. Now we know that it's global warming. Why did one threat fade while the other grew? The Montreal Protocol of 1987 laid out a strategy to combat ozone depletion. Nations of the world committed to the sacrifices the Protocol demanded, and it now seems that this particular environmental threat has been dodged. Buoyed by our success with ozone depletion, the world set about neutralizing the threat of global warming through the Kyoto Protocol of 1992, which was signed by 124 nations. Sadly, the United States led the resistance to the implementation of that treaty. Thus, combating global warming was crippled by our actions, and conditions are now worse than they were when the Kyoto Protocol was drawn up.

For thirty years, my career as a scientist has made me carefully study scientific predictions. The most insightful comment I've encountered came from an environmentalist who observed, "Realities don't cease to exist because we ignore them." The consequences of our actions will come due, sooner or later. Because a truly distributed energy system lies so far into our future (even if it immediately became our highest priority), I think that federal and state governments should incentivize the repair of our electricity grid. This conclusion could be stated more positively by noting that the grid will be an important resource whether we continue burning hydrocarbons, go to an all-electricity economy, or embrace a hydrogen-electricity economy.

Furthermore, because various threats (e.g., peak oil, global warming, wars over resources) draw closer by the day, it is good that so many states (California, Arizona, Oregon, Illinois, New Jersey, etc.) and so many corporations (*Wal-Mart, Proctor & Gamble, Home Depot*, etc.) have aggressively pursued alternative energy projects. There is still hope that we will be ready for our next energy/environmental crisis. Sadly, over the last decade (and in spite of the Herculean efforts of a few politicians), the Federal Government has done virtually nothing to foster true alternative energy sources (e.g., solar, wind, geothermal, tides). Subsequent generations will charge us with political malpractice. We will be forced to explain why we fiddled while oil, coal and gas burned.

Chapter 9

Pity the Poor Politicians

Imagine you are a member of the U.S. House of Representatives who is considering voting to require utilities to get 15% of their electricity from alternative sources (like solar). An opponent presents you with information arguing against solar. Some excerpts include:

> With "free energy" shining down, it should be expected people would want to harness solar energy to replace polluting sources of electricity. Is this possible? Yes, but the question is not whether some source of energy *could* provide the amount of energy necessary to fuel our energy-driven economy, but whether or not it is a *practical* solution for providing electrical energy sufficient for individuals. After all, even moonbeams have energy and, with a sufficiently large and effective collection and generation system, energy could be harnessed from moonbeams. But it's not practical to do so, one reason being that the collection panels would have to be huge. The problem with solar generation is the same as for moonbeams, the difference being only in degree…
>
> The trouble occurs when very large amounts of power must be generated and available at all times. Not all solar energy is converted to electricity in photovoltaic cells, and not from want of trying. The photovoltaic effect is produced by sunlight of a particular frequency (color) causing silicon—that has been "doped" with special imputs—to give up electrons. The part of the sunlight spectrum with a lower frequency doesn't have the energy to cause electrons to be ejected. [Au: This is *not* true of *UNISOLAR* cells.] Energy from higher frequency solar

radiation is largely lost to heat after it has done its job of "kicking out" an electron. The problem of maximizing power from sunlight has been known for at least 30 years, and is primarily one of physical limitations, not engineering technology.

In order to calculate the average output from a photovoltaic array, one would take the insolation per square meter or acre, allow for needed spacing, and multiply by the efficiency of the photovoltaic cell. Let's check what power could be generated in Albuquerque. Commercial photovoltaic cells turn about 10 percent of the sun's energy into electrical energy and, in order to keep the PV cells clear to direct them toward the sun, 50-percent spacing is typical. [Au: *UNI-SOLAR* cells work with less than 5% spacing.]

Doing the math, an acre of land with solar-cell arrays with 50-percent spacing in Albuquerque would theoretically produce an average of 48.5kw. That is a bit of power—enough for about 40 hand-held hair dryers, or eight to 10 kitchen ranges—but to get it requires an area four-fifths the size of a football field covered with expensive semi-conductors and miles of inter-wiring, not to mention inverters and transformers, to produce usable electricity. Because of its lower insolation, Hartford, Connecticut, would generate one-third less or 32.3 kw per acre. This is equivalent to 24 horsepower—not exactly what is needed to power homes, community services, and industrial needs...

• How do you propose to replace existing power plants when statistically there will be extensive periods when both wind and solar power will not supply *any* energy to the power grid?

• How can you say that wind and solar power can significantly reduce carbon dioxide emissions when utilities must maintain on-line, fuel-burning "spinning reserves" to be instantly able to produce power when wind or solar sources suddenly stop?

Notice how "scientific" this information sounds. It's not highly emotional or extreme. It's no wonder that a politician might find it plausible. Yet, it *misrepresents* the role solar can play in meeting society's energy needs. In order to see the flaws in the above arguments, one must know far more about how electricity is actually produced and used than the critique above reports. Consider the following example.

Electricity plants are categorized as either base plants or peaker plants. Base plants are run 24 hours a day and 7 days a week. Base plants are either plants that cannot be turned off (e.g., hydro) or plants that produce power as cheaply as possible (e.g., coal). Peaker plants are only turned on when peak time power demands come close to exceeding base electricity production. Peaker plants typically produce the most expensive electricity (usually via natural gas), but that power is both less polluting and releases fewer greenhouse gases than coal-powered, base plants. Figure 9-1 shows a fictitious utility that has nine base plants (labeled A through I).

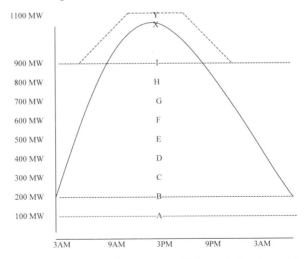

Figure 9-1. Depiction of sources of electricity for a fictitious utility throughout a day.

If the average base plant produces 100 MW of power, then the nine base plants produce 900 MW. Point X is the utility's peak power demand on a hot July day. Thus, we need to add two peaker plants (<10 hrs./day) to the nine base plants (24 hrs./day) to meet the maximum energy demand of almost 1100 MW of power.

An alternative would be to add 200 MW of solar power from photovoltaic cells (which is actually quite easily done) on roofs of homes and businesses in the utility's cachement. This is shown by the highest dashed line (Point Y). Would the addition of 200 MW of solar power eliminate the need for the two peaker plants for ten hours? Yes, but any smart utility would remove two of its most repulsive coal-fired, high polluting base plants (e.g., A and B) for the entire 24-hour period! This process is what's called "peak shaving." Photovoltaic cells remove the need for dirty coal-fired plants all day and all night *even though solar cells only produce during the daytime.* By adding 200 MW of solar capacity, we need only *seven* base plants (24 hrs./day) and two peaker plants (< 10 hrs./day) to meet the same energy demand of almost 1100 MW of power.

What has America lost if we simply install the 200MW of solar cells? Actually, some coal miners will no longer be required to produce coal. However, these miners might be better off not braving the dangers of mine disasters, black lung disease, and so forth. Would you rather be a miner or be employed as a technician or a laborer in a photovoltaic or wind turbine factory?

Consider once again the two questions asked at the end of the critique of solar excerpted above. Although there are long periods when solar produces no energy (e.g., at night), the remaining seven base plants are more than capable of meeting the nighttime demand. Unfortunately, the defenders of the status quo will always be with us. Also, let's admit that the monied, hydrocarbon interests of the 21st Century are better at political infighting than were the Thaddeus Horsehides of the 20th Century. Sadly, that's a bad omen for our sons and daughters, should they ever be forced to fight a World War III. Let's hope that the gutting of the Energy Act of 2007 for solar, wind and a Renewable Energy Standard does not cripple us in fighting the Energy Crisis of 201?.

So to my representatives in Congress who voted for the *original* Energy Act of 2007, I'd like to say, "Congratulations on a job very well done. Hopefully, in 2009, with the next Congress (after the 2008 election) we will have even more people who think like you." Remember, as Alan Greenspan noted, "Sometimes the duty of political leadership is to convince constituencies that they are just plain wrong." Don't for a minute doubt the direction we must travel to get to an alternative energy-powered world. Now once again, imagine you are a member of the U.S. House of Representatives who is considering voting to require utilities to get 15% of their electricity from alternative sources (like solar). An opponent presents you with information arguing against solar. Are you ready to challenge flawed arguments?

California: A Political Leader

Tracing the history of California's huge lead in alternative energy is a difficult challenge, as there are countless threads that might be given more or less prominence in the story. For example, the California Air Resources Board was formed more than forty years ago. When telling the story of the change from gasoline to hydrogen in *Zoom: The global race to fuel the car of the future*, Carson and Vaitheeswaran, correctly identify the central, positive role that the California Air Resources Board played. [For an unsavory chapter in the Air Resources Board's long and distinguished history, see the movie *Who killed the electric car?*] Since this book focuses upon electricity and its non-transportation uses, I will highlight a different thread in California's alternative energy history.

California suffered tremendously in the *Enron*-aided electricity crisis of 2004. While California led all other states in the generation of alternative energy at that time, the amount it produced was still far too small to shield the state from the crisis in the price of natural gas that occurred. That crisis eventually led to huge increases in electricity rates in California. *Inovateus Development* recently quoted payback times for the same solar installation to be located by a corporation in either California or Indiana (see p. 31). How much is the solar electricity worth if the plant is located in California versus in Indiana?

California's electricity was worth $11,164 per year, whereas Indiana's electricity (from the exact same photovoltaic array) was worth a mere $4,176. Thus, one can easily see why approximately 30% of California's electricity is produced by alternative means (solar, wind, tides, geothermal, etc.), whereas less than 1% of Indiana's power comes from alternative sources.

In my opinion, states like Indiana continue to dig themselves into an energy hole from which it will be extremely difficult to emerge. Their lack of foresight makes it very difficult for individuals or businesses to "do the right thing" within their state borders. While California continues to lead, other states are sometimes reluctant to even follow. The 21st Century will not be kind to those states that lag too far behind because every increase in utility rates acts as if it was a green tax. However, while Indiana will pay 99% of the green tax increase, a comparable California resident will pay only 70%. With every *Target, Wal-Mart, Lowes, Builders Square*, etc. that chooses to locate their solar installations in Sacramento rather than South Bend, the 99% versus 70% gap grows larger. Stated bluntly, Indiana state politicians have shown little foresight or political leadership on this dimension, while California politicians continue to lead the way to a cleaner, more sustainable future.

Solar and/or Nuclear

By now it should be clear that I see solar power as the pre-eminent method for obtaining energy in the second half of the 21st Century. Stan Ovshinsky's solar cells are virtually indestructible (not made of glass), flexible and lightweight. Almost every roof in the world is a potential installation site. As the efficiencies of mass production take effect, the price of solar will soon become competitive with grid produced electricity. The point of equalization of price (between grid and solar) will come very soon in cities like Las Vegas and Honolulu, and a bit later for places like Seattle and South Bend.

Solar is a plug-and-play system. Install the photovoltaic cells, and watch them produce electricity day after day for thirty, or forty, or fifty years. At this point, no one knows how long Stan's solar cells will last. It will take about forty more years before we know whether they last fifty years—and there is reason to believe they will continue to function even then. Sunlight will likely remain free of charge for millions of years to come. Finally, power washing the roof once a year represents the only recurring maintenance requirement for *UNI-SOLAR* solar cells. With continued improvements in their conversion (of light into electricity) efficiencies, their value will become overwhelming.

If *solar* is so obviously the technology of the future, why would anyone even consider the benefits of *nuclear* energy? Recall that in December, 2007, (not exactly ancient history) the U.S. Senate stripped the Energy Bill of 2007 of the RES and all incentives for solar and wind power. It is clear that Washington still lacks sufficient political vision and will—and that Americans will sooner or later pay the price for our leaders' lack of leadership. All of the eleventh hour changes in the Energy Bill of 2007 favored our hydrocarbon industries (e.g., oil, coal, natural gas, biofuels), some by gaining new incentives, others by not losing some of the incentives that were bestowed upon them in the Energy Bill of 2005.

Nuclear power, however, does not involve the burning of hydrocarbons. Thus, ample nuclear power would allow us to meet even the most stringent carbon emission reduction standards. Nuclear energy can furnish a substantial portion of our energy requirements while making no contribution to air pollution or to global warming. By building many nuclear plants, the top two environmental problems listed on p. 9 (global warming and securing our energy future) are attacked simultaneously. Further, nuclear plants are always base (rather than peaker) plants, as it is unwise to turn them on and off unless it is absolutely necessary to do so. Consider a nuclear modification of Figure 9-1 on p. 65. If the utility's baseload came from five *nuclear* 100 MW plants, its electricity output would be a straight horizontal line for 24 hours/day at the level of Point E. The daytime peak would easily be handled by (for example) 800 MW of installed *solar* power. In fact, this arrangement exceeds peak power demands (Point X) by several hundred megawatts. Will that unused electricity be wasted as is currently the case for excess electricity that is produced at night? Absolutely not.

Recall that hydrogen is stored electricity. Any solar power not needed at peak times would be run through water to produce hydrogen (or it might be stored in batteries in one's basement). The batteries (or the stored hydrogen) become our home's backup power system. Thus, nighttime electricity needs can be met with electricity from the backup batteries, or from hydrogen that might be fed into a fuel cell to yield electricity. This solar and nuclear solution works quite well (no air pollution, no greenhouse gases, relatively cheap, etc). However, while there are no new problems created by the solar portion of the system, nuclear power creates several well-known difficulties.

The storage of spent nuclear fuel for tens of thousands of years is a huge problem that is no closer to being solved now than it was fifty years ago. Terrorism is also a growing problem for the 21st Century. The next time terrorists seize a jet airliner, a nuclear power plant might be an attractive target. Finally, as the technological barriers to constructing true nuclear bombs and dirty nuclear bombs are lowered, and there is more "spent fuel" that needs to be transported and/or stored, the greater the possibilities for nuclear terrorist catastrophes. Human error (as in Three Mile Island, Chernobyl, etc.) is less likely with newer plant designs than was the case before. Still, human error is always possible. However, as bad as these problems are, they still pale in comparison with global warming.

In sum, if our country's next energy crisis were to come in the next ten years, then we are simply out of luck—and the gutting of the Energy Bill of 2007 will be seen by all as a colossal misstep. If the crisis were to arrive in ten to forty years, then the solar, nuclear, and hydrogen solution might enable us to effectively sidestep this potential catastrophe. If the crisis were to arrive after forty years, our best move might be to put most of our energies into building solar factories—insuring the geometric growth in product availability and the dramatic decline in the cost of solar cells that this strategy would create. The role of our political leaders in crafting well a viable roadmap to our energy independence is a crucially important challenge.

Chapter 10

Greet Our Future

While many (including me) speak authoritatively about the future of our energy systems, *no one knows for sure* what things will be like ten, fifty, or one hundred years from now. Still, it is important to speculate about what the future holds. So here goes.

Currently in the United States, alternative energy supplies roughly 3% of all our energy needs. Hydrocarbons supply another 60% and other sources (e.g., nuclear, hydro) supply the remainder. I'll not speculate about the future of these "other" sources. Thus, looking *only* at the hydrocarbon-produced and alternatives-produced energy, hydrocarbons currently supply over 95% while alternatives supply less than 5%.

What will this mix be in ten years? My guess is something like 85% for hydrocarbons and 15% for alternatives. Reasonable estimates for alternatives by others are as low as 10% and as high as 25%. More extreme estimates seem unreasonable to me. [Congress has called for 25% of our electricity to be produced in 2025 via alternative means. I would be shocked, but delighted, if the 25% figure was achieved that quickly.]

Fifty years from now, my guess is that 40% of our energy will be produced by burning hydrocarbons and 60% will come from alternatives. However, if the new President and Congress get behind alternative energy in a big way, alternatives might deliver 80% of our energy needs in fifty years, making my 60% prediction embarrassingly low. If our elected representatives declare (and follow through on) a Manhattan Project-style alternative energy initiative, the crossover from burning hydrocarbons to the age of hydricity will come very quickly.

One hundred years from now I think alternatives will supply over 98% of our energy needs. However, this dramatic reversal of the sources of energy will *not* come about for environmental reasons, but for economic ones. Our earth's ecosystems can handle the burning of some hydrocarbons—just not our current profligate burning of hydrocarbons. Rather, several hydrocarbons will be too expensive to find and produce (oil and natural gas). But even for plentiful hydrocarbon resources (like coal), it will be very difficult to compete with an energy source like solar, whose fuel cost is $0. As we recently became aware that our corn is too expensive to burn (as ethanol), so too in the future, will we come to recognize that other hydrocarbon sources of energy will also be too expensive to burn.

If I Were President

> In the heyday of nationwide preparations for the 1978 celebration of Sun Day, it may have appeared that the United States was on the verge of wholehearted, broad-based adoption of solar and other renewable technologies as crucial components in the energy mix. Since this never occurred, it is critical to consider the rise and fall of solar advocacy during a watershed period. (p. 12)

In their book, *Who owns the sun?*, Berman and O'Connor provide an explicit analysis of how hydrocarbon producers (e.g., oil, coal) and users (e.g., electric companies, railroads) crushed a promising competing technology—solar energy—thirty years ago. Now we again face an important question. Will we move in a similar direction? Or have we learned our lesson from the past, and now recognize solar's importance for the world's future?

There is ample reason for hope. Huge corporations like *GE*, *GM*, *Wal-Mart*, *Google*, *P&G*, and many others are aggressively pursuing solar programs. Even some hydrocarbon corporations (e.g., *BP*, *Chevron*) are declaring themselves to be energy companies rather than just hydrocarbon companies. One hopes they now see the wisdom of helping solar to quickly achieve its potential.

If I were President, I would do exactly what Congress attempted to do in the Energy Bill of 2007 that was rebuffed by a coalition of Republican senators and one Democrat from Louisiana. I would install a Renewable Energy Standard and further incentivize solar, wind, and geothermal. If I had to pay for these incentives, I'd take back some of the incentives that were given away in the Energy Bill of 2005 to hydrocarbon companies.

Second, I would do everything in my power to facilitate the building of thousands of photovoltaic factories, and offer incentives to help consumers purchase solar cells. I would charge the Secretary of Energy to determine the companies with the most scientifically promising solar and wind technologies that are currently in (or close to) production of their products. I would have the Secretary do everything necessary (through grants, guaranteed loans, etc.) to increase the production of products that we currently know are good.

Next, a greatly expanded pool of research dollars would be directed toward funding studies of the most commercially promising future technologies out there. This would maximize the supply side of the equation. Nothing more need be done to stimulate demand for alternative energy products beyond the RES and incentives mentioned earlier.

Powering our energy system with clean and renewable sources of electricity is clearly our first challenge. However, the implementation of the remainder of the hydrogen loop (see p. 20) must also be undertaken. Resistance to other parts of the hydrogen loop (e.g., fuel cells, hydrogen storage units, hydrogen distribution systems, and hydrogen production units) generally take the form of "It makes no sense to create one part of the system in the absence of the others." For example, why create a fuel cell auto when there currently is no system for cleanly and renewably producing hydrogen? Why produce large quantities of hydrogen when people cannot now buy affordable fuel cells? Unless one can envision a complete, workable system, developing any part of the system seems to be an endeavor fraught with risk.

I would begin the implementation of the hydrogen loop in the manner described in the Box labeled "Plunging Into the Hydrogen Loop." It gives a description of a plan for a university or a service station to collaborate with a utility to convert unused, off-peak electricity into large quantities of hydrogen.

Plunging Into the Hydrogen Loop

Because base plants generally run 24/7, there is often excess electricity that goes unused during off-peak hours. The dollar and environmental costs of this nighttime power have been incurred, and yet society sometimes receives little or nothing of value for such off-peak electricity. As society transitions from a hydrocarbon powered electric system to a hydrogen-electric system, the value of off-peak power will soar.

Autos of the future will be all-electric (pending solution of vexing lithium battery problems) and/or fuel cell-electric (like the *Chevy Volt*). Millions of pure electric autos would be charged primarily at night, thus virtually eliminating the peak/off-peak distinction, as off-peak electricity becomes as valuable as peak power. But what if lithium batteries are unable to solve their present cost and safety problems?

Then we would turn to the *Chevy Volt* architecture (due out in 2010), wherein a battery capable of going 40-50 miles on its own is constantly recharged by a small fuel cell. Such autos would carry on board enough hydrogen (i.e., 4-5 Kg of hydrogen) to extend the auto's range to over 300 miles. Refueling a *Volt*-like auto involves two steps. First, its large battery is recharged with grid-produced electricity overnight. Second, hydrogen is loaded on-board like gasoline. Where and how will this hydrogen be produced?

I propose that electric companies everywhere convert excess off-peak power into hydrogen at their power plants. This hydrogen could then be distributed to service stations and sold everywhere alongside gasoline. At the utility facility, the hydrogen can serve as a daily peaker plant. This is the large-scale production model.

Alternatively, a small-scale production model would eliminate the need for distribution and transportation of the hydrogen. We might conduct the small-scale demonstration at a service station or at a university, where they create, on-site, as much hydrogen as needed to refill their hydrogen storage tanks using cheap, off-peak electricity. The university's hydrogen can be used to generate electricity directly, to power converted boilers, and/or to be sold at local service stations.

I propose we build and test both the large-scale and small-scale models to demonstrate their different efficiencies and costs. One could write grants (to cover the equipment costs of these experiments) which should be easy to obtain as all of these activities constitute renewable energy projects.

Both the utility, the service station, and the university can, at the very least, convert unused, off-peak electricity into clean peak electricity. However, the hydrogen might be put to even better use. Engage a fuel cell company and a company with a safe means for storing hydrogen, and the hydrogen infrastructure begins to take shape. Finally, engage an auto company to build hydrogen fuel cell autos, knowing that electric companies anywhere could implement the off-peak electricity to hydrogen program, thus making hydrogen available virtually anywhere. Another benefit of this new hydrogen-electric system would be to provide a back-up power system (i.e., the fuel cell auto) to every home. These are the sorts of programs that any forward-looking politician ought to endorse. But even with a totally supportive administration, we are still not yet out of the woods. We still need to get lucky with time.

We Know Not the Day Nor the Hour...

Octavio Paz says, "We are condemned to kill time. Thus we die bit by bit." For energy use, the end of the age of burning hydrocarbons is clearly in sight. However, the age of renewables, like solar, wind and hydrogen, is still only a chimera on the horizon. If we knew we possessed fifty years to transition to solar and hydrogen, our present pace would be adequate. But our next energy crisis (e.g., peak oil, a tipping point for global warming, another war in the Middle East, a successful terrorist attack on the oil infrastructure, etc.) might already be history by the time this book is printed. If our time is short, we will have died bit by bit because we wasted the last sixteen years.

From 1992 to 2008, our politicians (one President a Democrat, the other a Republican) failed to provide the leadership that was desperately needed to insure the smooth energy transition we required. With rare exception, our businesses also failed us. Undoubtedly this snail's pace was partially determined by the enormous amounts of money given to politicians by companies that grew wealthy on the sale of hydrocarbons. [In 2007, for example, *Exxon* made over $40 billion in profits—the largest profit any company ever made.]

Public opinion now has shifted in spite of the efforts of a few hydrocarbon-dependant industries and the lack of political courage and leadership by the majority of our politicians. One can see the shift reflected in the way politicians in both parties (in the Presidential primaries of early 2008) have sought to assert that they are the "greenest" candidate and are solidly behind "energy independence." So change will come in time. "Do we have enough time left?" now becomes the currently unanswerable question [see the movie *Crude awakening*].

Many have asserted that the change from hydrocarbons to hydrogen will be the largest industrial shift—and therefore the greatest business opportunity—in human history. This book is written for those who wish to make a change for the better. Some consumers have a simple task, such as to change from incandescent lightbulbs to compact fluorescents. Others are called upon to think through enormous changes for their corporations or for their political constituencies. My target readers throughout have been all citizens, and especially business executives and politicians called upon to take the risk of stepping into a better energy future. I wish all of us sufficient time to make these transitions safely. For as warned by countless environmentalists, "Realities don't cease to exist simply because we ignore them."

Our Challenge

Returning to the I = PAT formula (Chapter 2) one final time shows cause for hope. Worldwide population growth must be reined in. But some people simply want four children instead of the replacement value of 2.1 children per couple. Are such people doomed to being labeled as selfish or as bad citizens of the planet? Not necessarily. See the Box entitled "A Second Way."

A Second Way

The average woman (worldwide) now gives birth to about 3.6 children over her lifetime, while 2.1 children per woman would represent a replacement fertility rate. Suppose, for cultural or religious reasons, women *insisted* upon having four rather than two children. Mathematically, it is true that a woman who has four children beginning at about age thirty-six exerts far less population pressure on the earth than a woman who has only two children, but who begins having children at age eighteen. If parents start families later in life, it can benefit the earth and its ecosystems as much or more than if families actually reduced their families' sizes. A quick thought experiment will clarify this counterintuitive thought. See Figure 10-1.

Imagine a woman (G_0 in Figure 10-1 top panel) who has two children rather early in her life. Her first child might have been born in 1988 (when the mother was eighteen years old) and the second child born in 1992 (when the mother was twenty-two years old). Assume also that all her progeny will exhibit her same fertility pattern (i.e., two children, early births). The column on the left side of the figure gives the date of birth of the mother (G_0) and the average date of birth of all children in each subsequent generation (G_1, G_2 ...). The right hand column presents the number of people in each generation. In this hypothetical example, in the year 2052, the fifth generation would be complete, and a total of thirty-one people would be represented in this family tree.

The lower panel of Figure 10-1 is identical to the top panel except for two important changes. First, instead of having a below-replacement level fertility rate of two children per family, the mother (and all her descendants) will have four children per family. Second, we also double the mother's age at the time of birth of her average child. For example, the G_1 children might have been born in the years 2008, 2009, 2011, and 2012. In this instance, the family tree of people who have larger families later in life total only twenty-one members in the year 2052. This demonstrates the counterintuitive reality that efforts directed toward having people delay their child-bearing years can be even more helpful than efforts to reduce family size.

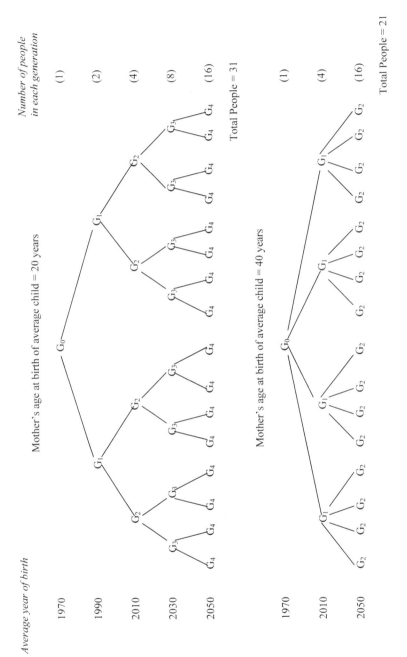

Figure 10-1. A second way to reduce population growth.

So now one has two ways to help curb population growth: have smaller families and/or have families later in life.

In our final look at I = PAT, we must also closely examine the T-term. Coal production of electricity has a high T-value, and so we stress (I) our ecosystems greatly when we obtain energy in that manner. However, using cogeneration reduces the T-value somewhat, and therefore produces less stress on the environment. Furthermore, when we obtain electricity via *UNI-SOLAR* photovoltaics, the T-value is vanishingly small—virtually 0! What happens when a T-value is an infinitesimal fraction? Large numbers of people (P) can lead lives of high affluence (A) while imposing almost no stress (I) on our ecosystems.

Thus, the top two environmental problems (global warming and energy, see Chapter 2) will be dealt severe blows when we switch to obtaining our electric energy from clean and renewable photovoltaics. In fact, the third ranked environmental problem (obtaining pure water) is also greatly improved by widespread use of photovoltaics, as desalination of sea water is possible when clean, renewable energy is plentiful. Solar doesn't solve all of our environmental problems, but it can take a huge bite out of our three worst problems. As Stan Ovshinsky and Tom Kanczuzewski have long maintained, solar appears to be the logical place to begin our march toward a better world.

References

Berman, D. M. & O'Connor, J. T. (1996). *Who owns the sun? People, politics, and the struggle for a solar economy.* White River Junction, VT: Chelsea Green.

Carson, I. & Vaitheeswaran, V. (2007). *Zoom: The global race to fuel the car of the future.*

Carson, R. (1962). *Silent spring.* Boston: Houghton Mifflin.

Ehrlich, P. (1968). *The population bomb.* New York: Ballantine.

Ehrlich, P. & Ehrlich, A. (1990). *The population explosion.* New York: Simon & Schuster.

Goodell, J. (2006). *Big coal: The dirty secret behind America's energy future.* Boston: Houghton Mifflin.

Greenspan, A. (2007). *The age of turbulence.* New York: Penguin Press.

Hardin, G. (1993). *The ecology of commerce.* New York: Harper Collins.

Hawkin, P. (1993). *Living within limits: Ecology, evolution and population taboos.* New York: Oxford Press.

Henderson, H. (1981). *The politics of the solar alternatives to the economics age.* Garden City, NY: Anchor/Doubleday.

Howard, G. S. (2002). *How should I live my life? Psychology environmental science and moral traditions.* Notre Dame, IN: Academic Publications.

Howard, G. S. (2006). *Stan Ovshinsky and the hydrogen economy: Creating a better world.* Notre Dame, IN: Academic Publications.

Lerch, D. (2007). *Post carbon cities: Planning for energy and climate uncertainty.* New York: Post Carbon Press.

Malthus, T. (1798). "An essay on the principle of population." In G. Hardin (ed.) 1964. *Population, evolution and birth control.* San Francisco: Freedman.

Meadows, D. H., Meadows, D. L. & Randers, J. (1992). *Beyond the limits.* Post Mills, VT: Chelsea Green.

Simmons, M. (2006). *Is oil running out?* New York: Global Public Media.

Appendix 1

Too Many People

The following is an excerpt from a 1973 paper by Professor John Holdren, "Population and the American Predicament: The Case Against Complacency," published the year after the Rockefeller Commission on Population and the American Future recommended to President Nixon and the public that America grow no more. It is a remarkably prescient piece written by a respected scientist on the subject of population size and impact.

Those who advocate the early attainment of zero population growth, or a return to a smaller population by way of a period of negative growth, are often challenged to name an "optimum" population figure and defend it. What, after all, is the point of stopping or turning around if we don't know what the optimum is? Perhaps it is actually larger than the present population. The question of the optimum is not an easy one, but I think one can make some sensible observations about it.

First, we can probably agree that the optimum and the maximum are not the same thing. The maximum population, or carrying capacity, is determined by such factors as usable land area, fertility of soils, availability of mineral resources and water, and the ability of biological systems to absorb civilization's wastes without breakdowns that deprive us of essential services. No one knows just what the maximum is or which limiting factor will determine it, and, in any case, the answer will almost certainly vary with time as technology changes. But in no event is a population size that is at or near the maximum likely to be optimum; if availability of resources defines the limit, the maximum implies bare subsistence for all;

if environmental constraints define it, the maximum is likely to represent a precariously unstable situation. By the same token, it is easy to imagine a population size smaller than the optimum—one, for example, too small to enjoy the benefits of specialization, economies of scale, and cultural diversity.

A general, and perhaps innocent, definition of the optimum population size is the size that permits the maximum average well-being per person. It is the definition of "well-being" that gets us into trouble, for this term clearly must include physical necessities such as food, water, shelter, and a livable environment; social essentials such as employment and economic security, education, and means for conflict resolution and the administration of justice; and amenities such as recreation and cultural pursuits. Not of all these values can be adequately reflected in the economic marketplace, and there are considerable differences in the relative importance that different groups and individuals would assign to the various ingredients. What is important to me—say, proximity to a great museum—may be unimportant to you compared to some other value—say, proximity to wilderness. Yet without consensus on what well-being consists of, how can we say anything useful about optimum population?

I believe that from these fundamental differences in human values an operationally useful conclusion does emerge; the concept of the optimum population hinges on the need for social, cultural and environmental diversity, for only thus can a wide variety of preferences be satisfied. At very low population sizes, the raw material for sufficient cultural and social diversity does not exist; near the physical maximum, on the other hand, diversity must be sacrificed in order to maximize efficiency.

From the individual's perspective, of course, diversity in the social and physical environments is related to personal options—access to a variety of employment possibilities, living accommodations, educational and recreational opportunities, degrees of privacy, and so forth. With respect to this criterion, then, one can say that the optimum population size is that beyond which further growth closes more options than it opens. The reader may wish to ponder what this definition implies in the case of the United States. For myself, I am unable to think of many options being opened by further population growth (greater variety in airline schedules?), but I can think of a good many that are being closed (the opportunity to escape congestion, to survive without an automobile, to live anywhere but in a city).

Of course the optimum population size and the maximum size are dynamic quantities, not static ones. "Optimum" should mean "optimum under existing social and technological conditions." To argue that a region is not overpopulated by pointing out that certain technical and social changes could, in time, relieve the population-related pressures there is to miss the point. Technological innovation and cultural evolution will no doubt lead to changes in the population size regarded as optimum, and perhaps will push up the maximum. But a prudent society will let its actual population conform to such changes as they occur, rather than hope blindly, as most do today, that technology and social change will render acceptable whatever degree of population growth happens to materialize.

My own suspicion is that the United States, with about 210 million people [in 1973], has considerably exceeded the optimum population size under existing conditions. It seems clear to me that we have already paid a high price in diversity to achieve our present size, and that our ability to elevate the average per capita level of well-being would be substantially greater if the population were smaller. I am also uneasy about the possibility that 280 million Americans [In 2007, the US is over 300 million and still growing quickly], under conditions likely to include per capita consumption of energy and materials substantially higher than today's, will prove to be beyond the environmentally sustainable maximum population size.

John P. Holdren is Teresa and John Heinz Professor of Environmental Policy and Director of the Program on Science, Technology, and Public Policy at the Kennedy School of Government at Harvard University. Professor Holdren is past president of the Association for the Advancement of Science (AAAS). "Population and the American Predicament: The Case Against Complacency" was first published in the Fall 1973 issue of *Daedalus* journal. *Reprinted with permission.*

Part of our difficulty in taking control of population problems is purely psychological. We have become a society that glorifies maximization as opposed to optimization. It is as if people believe that if something is "a good" (e.g., money, prayers, vacation, people) then having more "goods" must be a better state of affairs (Howard, 2002). While one might argue that for some goods (e.g., money) the maximum is the optimum, for most goods (e.g., prayers, people, vacations) the optimum is clearly less than the maximum. Might someone pray for eighteen to twenty hours each day? Perhaps. Should they? Absolutely not. Could the earth hold twenty billion people? Even if it could, life on that overpopulated planet would be nightmarish for all.

I have been arguing for population containment for almost two decades. [Paul Erlich has fought overpopulation for about half a century (cf. *The population bomb*, 1960).] But if you suggest that family size be limited, either by fiat or by a tax on each child, be prepared to duck.

The future is best predicted by mathematical models (e.g., economic, meteorologic). Our environmental future was probed by Meadows, Meadows and Randers (1992) who measured 225 environmental, economic, and energy variables over a ninety year period—almost the entire 20th Century. They then let the data create a mathematical model of the interrelationships among these 225 variables by modeling the interrelationships using the actual data of the ninety year period. Next they had the computer play forward (predict) the next few years on the target variables. Predicted data on these hypothesized interrelationships fit the actual data obtained quite well. This suggests that the model works reasonably well. Finally, the authors instructed the computer to predict the future of the 21st Century for the variables in this standard model (a model where the authors changed nothing). The planet continues its catastrophic population growth and begins to decline around the year 2030.

Historically, World War II was the greatest catastrophe the world has experienced thus far (when defined by the loss of lives) where approximately 100 million people died over a five year period (1941-1945). In the standard model, the earth's population declines from about eight billion to four billion over a long period of time. This would imply that more than four billion lives are lost (as normal births continue over this time period of crisis). In the standard model, pollution levels increased dramatically prior to a severe decline in per acre yield of agricultural output. Thus, food shortages are implicated in the catastrophe—although one can never know exactly how this scenario will actually play out from a mathematical model. For example, severe food shortages might precipitate a war that kills billions of humans. Conversely, all deaths might be due solely to starvation.

Several alternative models of the 21st Century were then tested (e.g., one where alternative energy funding was increased dramatically, one where funding for pollution control was greatly accelerated, etc.). All such models (save one type) pushed back catastrophe for several years, but the catastrophe occurred eventually.

The only models which eliminate a catastrophe in the 21st Century were ones where the increase in population was arrested quickly. In these sustainable models the earth's population sometimes rises to eight or more billion (because of population lag effects), where it then levels out. While all mathematical models are speculative (e.g., we all know the problems in accurately forecasting the weather) these particular glimpses of the future certainly suggest the wisdom of the saying, "No matter what your cause, it's a lost cause unless we first control population growth."

Whatever is the optimum human population of the earth, it is less than our present more than six and a half billion people. Passing that optimum value condemned us to having an overpopulation problem. Sadly, that passing was a silent event, with few, if any, of us noting its significance. It reminds me of the World War II saying addressed to soldiers who were terrorized by the noise of exploding bombs, "It's the one you don't hear that kills you."

The Box below entitled "Geometric Growth: Imagining the Unimaginable" was noted by *Reuters* in 2007.

Geometric Growth: Imagining the Unimaginable

United Arab Emirates — A one-legged father of 78 children is preparing for his next two marriages as he closes in on his target of having 100 children by 2015. Daad Mohammed Murad Abdul Rahman, 60, has already had 15 brides, though he divorces wives to make way for new ones in order to stay within the legal limit of four.

Daad Mohammed, retired truck-driver, policeman and soldier, lost a leg in a road accident and plans to have an artificial limb fitted in Jaipur in India—and while there he hopes to find one of his new brides. One more has already been lined up in Baluchistan, Pakistan.

"In 2015, I will be 68 years old and will have 100 children," he said. "After that I will stop marrying. I have to have at least three more marriages to hit the century. Two of my wives are pregnant and they will give birth within two months." Daad Mohammed is head of possibly the largest single UAE dynasty with 127 members, including 49 grandchildren, and has 15 houses.

Rewritten from Reuters, August 21, 2007

Now here is the unimaginable part: the current population of the world is 6.6 billion. If this man's descendants each have 78 children, how many offspring will this one man have after just six generations? He'll have 225 billion descendants—or 34 times the current population of the world!

One should never underestimate the power of geometric growth.

Appendix 2

The New York Times

NOVEMBER 11, 1968

Glassy Electronic Device May Surpass Transistor

By WILLIAM K. STEVENS

A Detroit inventor-scientist, in a long-awaited paper that is being published today, describes the production of electronic devices made from simple, inexpensive glassy materials that are said to promise practical benefits beyond what transistor technology can offer.

Stanford R. Ovshinsky, a 45-year-old, bushy-haired pipe smoker with the enthusiasm of a schoolboy, described the devices at a news conference in his office in Troy, Mich., last Friday, three days before the publication of his paper in Physical Review Letters, official journal of the American Physical Society.

Among the fruits of the versatile electronic components, Mr. Ovshinsky said, are expected to be small, general-purpose desktop computers for use in homes, schools and offices; a flat, tubeless television set that can be hung on the wall like a picture,

Stanford R. Ovshinsky, scientist-inventor, whose work with amorphous materials is said to promise practical benefits beyond what the current transistor technology can offer.

Continued on Page 42, Column 4

91

A New Science

On November, 11, 1968 a front page story in *The New York Times* entitled, "Glassy Electronic Device May Surpass Transistor"[1] attracted a great deal of attention:

> *A Detroit inventor-scientist, in a long-awaited paper that is being published today, describes the production of electronic devices made from simple, inexpensive glassy materials that are said to promise practical benefits beyond what transistor technology can offer.*
>
> *Stanford R. Ovshinsky, a 45-year-old, bushy-haired pipe smoker with the enthusiasm of a schoolboy, described the devices at a news conference in his office in Troy, Mich., last Friday, three days before the publication of his paper in **Physical Review Letters**, official journal of the American Physical Society.*
>
> *Among the fruits of the versatile electronic components, Mr. Ovshinsky said, are expected to be small, general-purpose desktop computers for use in homes, schools and offices; a flat, tubeless television set that can be hung on the wall like a picture, and missile guidance systems impervious to destruction by natural or man-made radiation.*
>
> *He added that the devices were expected to cut the cost and size of electronic systems generally.*
>
> *He said that his devices were made of amorphous materials—those with a disordered, irregular atomic structure—whose electrical properties were different from the atomically symmetrical, crystalline materials that transistors are made of.*
>
> *Ordinarily, the amorphous glasses block the flow of electricity. But the balance of energy forces inside them is such that when a voltage of just the right minimum, or threshold, strength is applied it makes the material suddenly switch from an insulator to a conductor.*

This property has been called the "Ovshinsky effect." The effect puts amorphous glasses in the class of semiconductors, which have been the foundation of the post-World War II electronics revolution.

Some of the world's leading solid-state physicists, interviewed last week, credited the discovery to Mr. Ovshinsky, viewed it as one of the most exciting developments in their field in some years and said it represented a departure in electronic technology.

"It is the newest, the biggest, the most exciting discovery in solid-state physics at the moment," said Sir Nevill Mott, director of the Cavendish Laboratory at Cambridge University in England, who was interviewed by telephone.

The discovery of the Ovshinsky effect was "quite unexpected," said Professor Mott, whose current interest is in the field of amorphous materials. He is an unpaid consultant to Energy Conversion Devices Inc., the company in Troy, Mich., that Mr. Ovshinsky founded to develop glass semiconductors.

Professor Mott said that the principle of the transistor, discovered in 1947, could originally have been figured out on the basis of old knowledge, but that the Ovshinsky effect represented totally new knowledge.

The reaction within the electronics industry to the possible applications of the devices has generally been one of caution. Although experts in some major industrial laboratories said last week that they believed the potential uses of the glass devices were exciting, they were reserving judgment until more was known and demonstrated.

Energy Conversion Devices, however, says that it has contracts or joint agreements with several major electronics companies who prefer not to be named for competitive reasons.

Mr. Ovshinsky said that electronic components smaller than one five-thousandth of an inch across, or one-third the size of the smallest transistors, could be made from the amorphous materials.

Such devices can be packed densely enough to produce a typewriter-size general-purpose computer for home use at relatively low cost, he said.

*The paper in **Physical Review Letters**, titled "Reversible Electrical Switching Phenomena in Disordered Structures,"[2] describes devices that change from an insulating to a conducting state in 150 trillionths of a second when a threshold voltage is applied.*

The action is something like the firing of a nerve cell. The threshold voltage for a device depends on its thickness and on which kind of glass is used.

Mr. Ovshinsky said that some of the materials returned to their nonconducting state immediately after firing, which meant that they had performed like an electronic switch.

Other kinds of amorphous materials stay in the conducting state indefinitely, without further need for electrical energy from outside, in which case they act like a computer memory storage mechanism by "freezing" in a given state.

This device can be restored to its previous insulating state at any time by feeding it a pulse of current.

This memory device is expected to be useful in computers. Mr. Ovshinsky said that it could be "read" without wiping out the information it carried; that no current was necessary to maintain the memory state, and that access could be gained to any given memory element instantly.

He said that no existing computer memory had all these capabilities, although some had one or two.

The technological importance of the discovery, Mr. Ovshinsky said, lies partly in the fact that the glass switches and memory elements are far simpler, cheaper, easier to make and smaller than conventional semiconductor components.

Semiconductors pass only a small electric current, compared with a metal. On the scale of conductivity, they lie between conductors and insulators.

Crystalline semiconductors, which have largely replaced vacuum tubes as basic electronic devices, are made to conduct electricity by adding small bits of impurities to the material.

This upsets the crystalline atomic structure slightly, in such a way that when an electric force is applied, a few electrons move from atom to atom through the material. This is conduction.

It is time-consuming and costly to grow semiconductor crystals and "inject" them with impurities. Often, too, many rejects result.

Since the conduction properties of amorphous materials are intrinsic, the need to grow a crystal or to "dope" one could be obviated.

Mr. Ovshinsky says this results in a higher yield of good devices and leads to lower costs.

The amorphous switching device described in today's **Physical Review Letters** *is made of 48 per cent tellurium, 30 per cent arsenic, 12 per cent silicon and 10 per cent germanium.*

Unlike crystalline semiconductors, the glass devices pass current in two directions. In handling alternating current, the kind that comes into most homes, it is not necessary therefore to fabricate complex and expensive devices, as is the case with crystalline semiconductors.

Unlike conventional semiconductors again, Mr. Ovshinsky said, the glass materials are unaffected by radiation. Energy Conversion Devices, in one of four military contracts it holds, is developing radiation-proof computer circuits for use in the guidance systems of Air Force missiles.

Another promising application, the inventor believes, will be in flat-screen television sets to be hung on the wall like pictures.

Operating on household current, the "ovonic" devices—the name chosen by Mr. Ovshinsky—can withstand the high voltages that must be borne by the switching elements that would activate light cells on the electroluminescent screen.

In the company's modest, one-story plant on the northern outskirts of Detroit, a pilot production line has been set up on which workers each day turn out 150,000 ovonic devices in the form of glass film 1-20th the thickness of a human hair.

Thin film technology has been around for some years but has never achieved its potential largely because crystalline semiconductor devices have not been successfully produced in that form. Entire circuits and entire computers can now be made of the film, Mr. Ovshinsky said.

Mr. Ovshinsky has talked generally of his findings before— some would say he has evangelized about them—and others have made glass semiconductors experimentally since the discovery of the Ovshinsky effect in the early 1960s.

But until today's publication in **Physical Review Letters***, none of the scientific data had been disclosed. Mr. Ovshinsky said that publication had been delayed until patents had been obtained.*

The company's 10 scientific consultants, some paid and some not, include Dr. Mott; Dr. Hellmut Fritzsche, professor of physics at the University of Chicago's James Franck Laboratory and a vice president of the company; Dr. Isidor I. Rabi of Columbia University, 1944 Nobel prizewinner in physics; Dr. Morrel H.

Cohen, director of the James Franck Institute, and Dr. David Turnbull, Gordon McKay Professor of Applied Physics at Harvard University.

William K. Stevens (1968)

The atomic structure of a crystalline material repeats itself many times over. Thus, if you have a piece of pure silicon and wish to study its atomic structure, it would not matter where in the material you looked first. The answer (the basic atomic configuration observed) would be the same from any part of the material. A characterization of any part of the material reveals all one needs to know about the structure of the entire material.

Scientists love simple rules that can explain a broad array of phenomena. For example, $E=mc^2$. What could be a simpler characterization of the relationship between energy and mass? Einstein was especially attracted to such simple scientific laws. For a while, philosophers of science suggested that "simplicity" was one of the basic characteristics (along with predictive accuracy, internal consistency, external coherence, etc.) of good scientific theories. However, science in the last half of the twentieth century demonstrated that many areas of nature cannot be reduced to a few basic laws. Thus, simplicity is no longer considered a necessary requirement for good scientific explanations.

It was scientists' affection for simple explanations that drew them to the study of crystalline materials. That is, the regular periodic repetition of the basic structural elements made a theoretical and mathematical treatment of a substance possible. The repetition of a basic atomic structure throughout a material composed of trillions of atoms held the promise of some simple scientific explanations for each substance.

While the existence of disordered materials (and of glasses) was known for thousands of years, their disordered atomic structures discouraged further scientific scrutiny. It seemed unlikely that such materials would easily yield simple scientific explanations. However, in 1955, Stan and Iris turned their attention to the study of disordered and amorphous solids. They felt the most exciting physics lay in exploring this vast, unexplored ocean, using the periodic table as their nautical chart and their physical intuition as their compass. The remainder of this chapter will present an overview of the world of amorphous materials. While some parts may be challenging for readers with little science background, a precise understanding of the science is not necessary to appreciate the applications discussed in later chapters. For individuals who would like a more scientifically detailed explanation, Appendix 2, entitled "Amorphous and Disordered Materials—The Basis of New Industries," discusses the role of disorder.

What are the basic differences between crystalline and amorphous solids? Figure 6-1[3] gives pictures of amorphous and crystalline materials, showing differences between the two. In crystals, atoms are arranged in a regular, orderly fashion. This allows for the growing of, for example, silicon crystals that can then be sliced into (in the hundreds of microns range) wafers such that the marvels of modern electronic circuits can be etched and diffused into them. Such wafers are used for making solar energy collection cells as well as for making semiconductor chips.

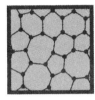

Figure 6-1

In contrast, the positioning of atoms in amorphous materials is completely disordered except for the nearest neighbors. And, very importantly, materials can be made much smaller than 100 angstroms, depending upon one's purpose. Furthermore, because they are noncrystalline, these materials, can be made over a very large area. For example, the Ovonic photovoltaic solar cells are manufactured by the mile as multi-layered thin films in a continuous process.

Back in the 1960s, scientists had no idea of how to characterize the properties of amorphous semiconductors. Whatever had been learned about solids was theoretically based on the crystalline, orderly arrangement of atoms. Disordered materials was not simply a new area, it required the development of a whole new science. Stan and his collaborators had to develop new concepts, design new experiments, and so forth, to understand the electronic processes in amorphous, disordered materials.

Ovshinsky staked out an entirely new, unexplored territory of materials science. Academics at the finest universities on several continents (e.g., Stanford, Chicago, Yale, Brown, Penn State, Harvard and MIT in the United States) dropped what they were doing to study Stan's new, amorphous materials. These came to be known as Ovonic materials. According to Webster's dictionary, the etymology of "Ovonic" derives from OVshinsky + electrONIC = OVONIC.

Sir Nevill Mott, then the head of the Cavendish Laboratory at Cambridge University, met Stan in 1967. He was immediately challenged by Ovshinsky's discoveries and switched his research program to Ovonic materials. Ten years later, when Sir Nevill received the Nobel Prize for his work on amorphous materials, he thanked Stan in his acceptance speech, "for saving me from the stagnation of theoretical solid state physics at the time."

Two University of Chicago physicists, Hellmut Fritzsche (an outstanding experimental physicist) and Morrel Cohen (a brilliant theoretical physicist) have also been longtime collaborators with Stan. Their most celebrated collaboration appeared in *Physical Review Letters* and is a citation classic in their field.[4] In that important paper the trio presented the CFO (after Cohen, Fritzsche and Ovshinsky) model which guided subsequent work in amorphous semiconductor science. According to Hellmut Fritzsche, in *R&A*,

...Stan's intuition and deep understanding of the roles of different elements in his materials were ingenious. That more than our painstaking experiments determined our progress and led to specific material compositions for fast switching, for memory action and soon for optical phase-change memories... Stan's laboratories had become a Mecca for many of us from Stanford, Harvard, MIT, Penn State and Chicago. Stan attracted the best and we had exciting brainstorming sessions at the big round table with Stan and kept up with the latest ideas and experiments...To witness Stan's fertile mind at work was a truly deep experience that taught me how to get to the depth of difficult problems...

One of Stan's closest friends and collaborators, David Adler, from MIT, wrote the following in his Introduction to Stan's 1991 book of collected papers, entitled *Disordered Materials—Science and Technology, Selected Papers by Stanford R. Ovshinsky*, edited by David Adler, Brian Schwartz, and Marvin Silver:[5]

... Stanford R. Ovshinsky, a self-taught genius who was previously known in scientific circles primarily for his contributions to automation and neurophysiology, began working in the field in 1955, when almost all physicists believed that amorphous semiconductors could not even exist. Ovshinsky studied the high-field properties of a large number of these materials, and between 1958 and 1961 discovered and developed the two types of reversible switching phenomena which now bear his name. He not only investigated the switching behavior in detail and proposed a

wide number of potential applications, but he also developed the chemical and metallurgical basis for choosing the composition of the materials in order to optimize the desired characteristics, proposed mechanisms for the origin of the phenomena, and reached important conclusions about the physical nature of the materials at equilibrium and their electronic nonequilibrium properties…

Stan himself, in simplifying the role of disorder, explains it thus:

The key to amorphicity/disorder is that it offers many degrees of freedom for atomic design, while very good crystalline materials are very rigid in that they have repeating atoms which severely constrain the addition or removal of elements without destroying the electronic or chemical mechanisms for which the crystals are designed.

Such crystals, for example in a semiconductor, can only have additions of parts per million of an alien atom. This is called doping and these extremely slight additions change the character of, for example, the silicon crystal so that it has become the basis of the whole transistor industry.

Not only do we use our principles to make completely amorphous materials without crystallinity, but also mixed materials, even crystalline, that we can use to intervene in the material and do atomic engineering and synthesize countless new materials with unique electronic, physical and chemical mechanisms, opening up a whole new area of opportunity to advance materials science in a very major manner.

One can see now that a material's surface composition can be far more important than scientists had previously thought. Furthermore, engineering special orbital relationships between various atoms that have different internal configurations than were being used by classical materials scientists is key—especially being able to accomplish this in what is now called "nanoscale," although Stan called it "working at the quantum limits of a material."

Ovshinsky and his colleagues have been doing nanostructure science since the 1950s. They introduced chemists and materials science engineers to the significance of lone pair electrons (first described by Mark Kastner of MIT), coordinate bonding, the novel chemistry of defects, and the like. These characteristics of amorphous science allow for the atomic engineering of materials to obtain desired characteristics that never before existed. For example, ECD has atomically engineered a metal hydride powder that can incorporate hydrogen into its atomic structure; is desorbed at relatively low temperatures; possesses good kinetics (can be refueled quickly); is tolerant of a large number of absorption-desorption cycles; and so forth. [See Chapter 9.]

Creating such a material using only conventional crystalline materials has not been a promising avenue. But with their extensive knowledge of the principles of disordered materials, ECD scientists routinely perform such "miracles." Indeed, Ovshinsky's principles state that anytime and anyplace one can get positional, compositional, or translational disorder, even in crystalline material (especially as one enters the nanostructure range), it allows atomic engineering to synthesize many kinds of materials, and provide important new mechanisms (electrical, chemical, structural) that were prohibited by the tyranny of the crystalline lattice.

Disordered and amorphous materials stand our knowledge of catalysts on its head. About 25 years ago, at a Gordon conference, Stan claimed that catalytic sites on disordered catalysts of very small dimensions are more numerous than on crystalline materials. Furthermore, he said that these sites are responsive to atomic and orbital engineering, since one could get the smallest nanoparticles to form multi-element materials with added new dimensions of bonding and anti-bonding orbitals.

The conventional wisdom at the time held that clean surfaces were necessary for catalytic reaction sites. History has not been kind to Stan's doubters. Using his new ideas about disordered catalysts, Stan modified transition and rare earth metal alloys to increase the density of hydrogen storage sites and to speed up the necessary catalytic surface reactions. Stan's key idea here was to employ steric and atomic engineering with the d- and f-orbitals of transition and rare earth elements to control the electronic density and generate new hydrogen storage sites. This is accomplished by controlling the total interactive sites in the material achieving needed new configurations. It is important to note that Stan was the first to grasp the principle (that later became known as nanostructures) that very small particles or thin films may have the same chemical elements but they are bonded or anti-bonded very differently in surfaces than in bulk.

Stan has shown Table 6-1[6], on the following page, for many years as he spoke about nanostructures and the vital role amorphicity and disorder play in permitting new physics, chemistry, electronic mechanisms, etc. As a modern example, in 1992 an important patent on the use of nanoparticles for multi-junction photovoltaics was issued. This patent follows up Stan's work on amorphous materials which was begun in the 1950s. Several layers of his photovoltaics have been nanocrystalline since the beginning.

Since he was the first to describe intermediate order (and with his colleagues proved it existed), Stan had outlined the means for getting intermediate order and nanocrystallites by utilizing a simple rule: Make amorphous materials as close as possible to the crystalline state (or make a crystalline material as close as possible to the amorphous state) and then one can have intermediate order and/or nanocrystals. A sure way (in silicon) to make nanocrystals is with the controlled use of fluorine. Stan had shown years ago that adding fluorine to carbon could make micro- or nanocrystals of diamonds.

Table 6-1

ROLE OF DISORDER

- Disorder provides the degrees of freedom to design local order/environments

- Results in a Total Interactive Environment (TIE) with a distribution/ spectrum of bonding/non-binding sites

- Many new synthetic materials

- New physical, electronic and chemical mechanisms

- Amorphous = thin film large areas

SMALL PARTICLES HAVE UNIQUE PROPERTIES THAT BRIDGE THE GAP BETWEEN CRYSTALLINE AND AMORPHOUS SOLIDS

- Small geometry gives rise to new physics

- 50 Angstrom particles are "mostly surface" — gives rise to new topologies and unusual bonding configurations

- 21% of all atoms in a 50 Angstrom particle are on the surface and ~ 40% are within one atom of the surface

- Compositional disorder in multi-element nano-alloys is large in small particles… e.g. in a 50 Angstrom particle, each element in a 10 element alloy will show 3% variation in concentration just due to statistics

- Quantum confinement effects are apparent

- Band structure effects are disturbed

The practical consequences of Stan's novel treatment of catalysts are staggering. He developed truly innovative electrode pairs for nickel-metal hydride batteries that now outperform all other propulsion batteries, and are now in use for all hybrid, electric, and fuel cell vehicles. [See Chapter 8.]

Stan's approaches have resulted in breakthroughs in the atomic engineering of disordered materials. But he is far more than a creative materials scientist. He is also a creative industrialist. He invents the materials, the products, and the production technology. His production processes are directly related to the physics and chemistry which are embodied in new products such as the Ovonic solar cells.

A number of years ago, various labs demonstrated amorphous silicon cells on glass plates which were not much bigger than the point of a pen. When they went into production with larger areas, they used batch processing on heavy breakable glass. But Stan had a better idea—a much bigger and better idea. He said, "We can produce solar devices by the mile, as one prints a newspaper—some cells being less than 100 angstroms in size." Thus, astonishingly early, when the solar cells indeed were very small, Stan envisioned and planned such production by the mile with a roll-to-roll machine on a flexible substrate with multi-junctions to capture more of the sun's spectrum and with materials which were much more efficient. His use of fluorine to make nanocrystalline layers was a most important innovation and gave him an enormous competitive edge. All had assumed such cells would be strung together in series to form solar arrays, as is still the case with crystalline photovoltaic cells. [See Chapter 7.]

Stan chose not to use paper or glass as the solar cell's backing but instead uses flexible substrates like thin sheets of plastic or stainless steel. These substrates proceed through chambers, as layer after layer of atomically engineered amorphous silicon (each layer 100 times thinner than a sheet of newspaper) is deposited one upon another. The layers are atomically engineered to absorb light from different parts of the light spectrum. Once through the machine, the cells are sometimes cut into shingles. Instead of covering a roof with "regular" shingles, one can now install an "electricity plant" of shingles for the roof which provides protection from the elements and looks like any traditionally shingled roof. Other solar cell configurations are available for standing seam metal roofs. They are not heavy or breakable and are aesthetically pleasing.

The current Ovonic photovoltaic production machine is the 8th generation of this line and is longer than a football field. Stan credits a splendid machine building team, and Herb Ovshinsky, his brother, who continues to play a key role in developing detailed designs of the continuous roll-to-roll machines. He emphasizes the true team effort of the engineers, scientists, and production personnel whose talent, dedication and commitment have done so much to make Ovonic photovoltaics manufacturing and operation so successful.

To say that Stan has built a better mousetrap is to lie by understatement. Some day when you are in the Auburn Hills, Michigan area, stop by the United Solar Ovonic Corporation plant. Who knows? If you are uncommonly lucky, someone might treat you to a tour of "the mother of all mousetraps."

Now to the information side of ECD's businesses, the opposite of the energy side of the same coin. Stan considers information to be encoded energy, and uses the same principles for both. Computer chips based upon amorphous and nonvolatile phase change materials, instead of the well-known crystalline transistors and other conventional devices, could well rule the future of the computer industry.

In 1999, Stan, through ECD, formed Ovonyx with Tyler Lowrey, former Vice-Chairman and Chief Technical Officer of Micron Technologies, to further commercialize his inventions in the information field, particularly Ovonic Universal Memory (OUM) technology. In February, 2000, Ovonyx and Intel entered into a collaboration and royalty-bearing license to jointly develop and commercialize OUM technology. Agreements with other chip production giants like STMicroelectronics, BAE Systems, Elpida, and others were quickly inked. There are many companies that have entered the field now, like IBM and Samsung. Others are joining the field, and in due course will become licensees. What are these chip giants so excited about?

OUM is a robust, high speed, nonvolatile memory that promises large advantages over, for example, widely-used FLASH memory (in cell phones, digital cameras, PDAs, etc.). These advantages include: 1) reduced cost per bit; 2) lower power requirements; 3) low voltage; 4) wide temperature range; 5) high scalability; 6) high speed; 7) nonvolatility; 8) multiple-bit storage per cell; and 9) radiation hardness. OUM also has advantages over other memory types such as DRAM, embedded applications, SRAM, and others.

The disordered world has opened a cornucopia of exciting possibilities in the materials science realm. The Ovonic threshold switch and the Ovonic three terminal replacement of conventional transistors are smaller, faster, and carry 50-times the current. As the semiconductor people say, "they scale"—which a transistor does not. And the ultimate computer is the Ovonic Cognitive Computer. [See Chapter 11.] Stan and ECD have led the charge with amorphous and disordered materials and products for over 45 years. And yet, it looks like the best is still to come in this exciting domain.

Science: Pure and Applied

Brian Schwartz is a condensed matter physicist at CUNY who has been active in the theory of disordered and amorphous materials over the years. Like many other scientists, he first heard of Stan from reading the front page of *The New York Times*, business and technology magazines. In the mid-1960s, Schwartz arrived at MIT as a researcher, first at the National Magnet Laboratory and later as a faculty member of the physics department. As he describes,

> *...these were vigorous and heady days for science and scientists, especially in the field of physics. The post-Sputnik American emphasis and encouragement of science and engineering had resulted in the commitment of significant new resources to science with a concomitant increase in research opportunities and engineering applications for materials science. As examples, the post-war discovery of the transistor was being used in electronic systems and miniaturized through integrated circuitry; the theory of superconductivity and the discovery of high-field type II materials enabled high-field superconducting magnets which changed the nature of high energy physics and found its way into medicine via the development of MRI techniques and the associated magnet systems. Having entered physics prior to the Sputnik impulse, I was one of the new young scientists riding the wave. During the "golden" decade of the 1960s, the addition of large numbers of young scientists to the research enterprise led to many important discoveries in basic and applied science. The young scientists complimented the much smaller group of more senior scientists, many of whom had contributed to the war effort of the United States in the Manhattan project or in other technologies such as the development of radar.*
>
> *At MIT, Harvard and the greater Boston area there was a group of young theorists in the field of Solid State Physics (now Condensed Matter Physics) who would meet periodically over lunch and at colloquia and seminars... Through Dave Adler's*

scientific collaboration with Stan Ovshinsky, I eventually got to meet Stan and began a long and fruitful relationship. I got to know many of the researchers at ECD… Throughout the 1970s I had informal and periodic encounters with Stan and ECD.

In the 1980s…ECD continued to make progress especially in the area of amorphous materials as applied to photovoltaic materials, and switching and memory devices. The company ECD had grown and was beginning to get recognition from the energy community. After signing a contract with BP for a significant research and development program especially in photovoltaics, I had the opportunity to become a regular consultant to ECD with specific tasks in the areas of materials research, especially superconductors (and later high temperature superconductors)…

Brian also served as the Director of the Institute for Amorphous Studies, which was founded in 1982 in Bloomfield Hills, Michigan, to promote the understanding of amorphous materials and their application. The Institute sponsored a lecture/seminar series, as well as a book series in conjunction with Plenum Press. Between 1985 and 1991, nine books were published in the series to disseminate the best research in the field of amorphous materials.

One of the Institute's early brochures provided the following overview:[7]

New materials and their understanding have always been the basis for advances in civilization. Historians and anthropologists have often categorized ages of humankind, such as the Stone Age, the Bronze Age, and the Iron Age, by the introduction of tools and techniques created by inventive uses of new materials. As we prepare for the 21ˢᵗ century, new synthetic materials based on freedom from crystalline constraints are emerging. These disordered, or amorphous, materials will be central to the solution of humankind's problems in energy, communications, and information processing, and the basis for many new materials needed for our changing industrial society…

Stanford Ovshinsky and his colleagues at Energy Conversion Devices have provided the key principles for the understanding of amorphous materials. They discovered that amorphous materials can exhibit certain unique properties that have never been observed in crystalline materials. It is now clear that structures free from crystalline constraints represent tremendous advances in flexibility.

The principles that they developed for understanding the properties of amorphous structures transcend materials science and are relevant to contemporary problems in physics, chemistry, and biology, including neurophysiology, the origins of life, and cosmology. Such concepts as phase transformations, supercooling, freezing in of defects, nucleation, and broken symmetry are becoming the common language for researchers in these frontier areas of science. Amorphous materials can be a catalyst for the transformation of crystalline thought into new and liberating paradigms for understanding the physical world...

[I]t is the ability to synthesize a myriad of new materials with new and unique physical, chemical, and electronic properties which makes amorphous materials so exciting both for their scientific value and their technological potential. The ability to engineer such materials results from the elimination of the restrictions of the crystalline lattice. The freedom to place atoms in three-dimensional space that this affords is the great potential of amorphous materials...

It is rather amazing that amorphous materials were classified as liquids for so long, especially since most of the solids we encounter in everyday experience are amorphous rather than crystalline. These include glass, plastics, rubber, and leather. Glass has many attributes: it is transparent, noncorrosive, inexpensive, and can be decorative. It is relatively dense and quite breakable. Plastics are now designed for a whole array of different uses. Both glasses and plastics are used in what we now call "passive" applications, e.g., packaging. With the rise of the electronics industry, there has been an intense effort in the design of "active" materials, those which generate or conduct and control electricity under certain circumstances. It perhaps came as a surprise to many scientists that amorphous materials exhibit the same gamut of electronic properties as crystals—they can be magnetic, transparent or opaque, insulating, semiconducting, metallic, or even superconducting...

There are many applications for active amorphous solids, just as there are increasing applications for passive amorphous materials. In the active area, amorphous materials are used for a wide spectrum of devices such as switches, memories and transistors, optical memories, photoreceptors, copying drums, television pick-up tubes, etc. In recent years, efficient, low-cost photovoltaic devices based on amorphous semiconductors have been developed, including solar

*cells for power generation and light-activated cells for consumer
electronics (e.g., hand calculators). Amorphous materials will
soon revolutionize the microelectronics and information processing markets, finding unique applications in large-area electronics,
flat-screen displays, erasable video disks, optical data storage, and
a host of other areas. Amorphous switching devices, having played
a crucial catalytic role in the development of nonvolatile program-
mable memories, should soon make their mark in computer control
and telecommunications applications. In addition, x-ray mirrors,
thermoelectric devices, and batteries employing amorphous and
disordered materials have been developed. It is clear that this long-
neglected class of solids is on the threshold of becoming the most
important class.*

Stan is an applied researcher, as his hydrogen loop represents a
thoroughly practical solution to many of society's energy problems
in the twenty-first century. However, right from the start, Stan has
also taken pains to conduct research that has high theoretical import.
Stan has more than 300 published articles and papers, some in the
finest physics and materials science journals in the world. His published papers range from neurophysiology to cosmology. Appendix
12 presents a partial list of Stan Ovshinsky's scientific journal articles,
book chapters and conference papers. Clearly Stan has bridged the
theoretical-applied chasm in science in a most productive manner.

Appendix 2 Footnotes

[1]Stevens, William K., "Glassy Electronic Device May Surpass Transistor." *The New York Times* (November 11, 1968, Pages 1 & 42).

[2]Stanford Ovshinksy. "Reversible Electrical Switching Phenomena in Disordered Structures." *Physical Review Letters,* November, 1968.

[3]*www.ovonic.com*

[4]M.H. Cohen, H. Fritzsche and S.R. Ovshinksky. "Simple Band Model for Amorphous Semiconducting Alloys." *Physical Review Letters*, May, 1969.

[5]David Adler, Brian Schwartz, and Marvin Silver (Eds.). *Disordered Materials—Science and Technology, Selected Papers by Stanford R. Ovshinsky*, 1991, New York: Plenum Press.

[6]Personal Communication.

[7]David Adler, S.R. Ovshinsky, and Brian Schwartz, "Introduction to the Institute for Amorphous Studies." (pamphlet produced by the Institute for Amorphous Studies, 1985).

Appendix 3

Subhendu Guha, Secretary of Energy Samuel Bodman, Iris, Stan, and Bob Stempel at United Solar Ovonic

Photovoltaics

One very vivid memory I have is in Stan's and Iris' home with a number of key employees, where Stan outlined his concept to manufacture photovoltaic cells in a revolutionary way like newsprint or photographic film. For those who have witnessed first hand the miracle of production of photovoltaic cells from our existing production equipment, it may not seem as impossible as it did to us, but in the late 1970s when "large area cells" were measured in centimeters, Stan's concept was beyond revolutionary—beyond comprehension. Nearly everyone in the group was skeptical that it would ever work. ECD, under Stan's leadership, has built many generations of roll-to-roll photovoltaic production machines culminating in the latest 30-megawatt plant that has earned the acclaim of people throughout the world. Observing Stan over the years, I have learned that when he tells me something is important, I don't have to understand it but can count on his vision and intuition.

Nancy Bacon
Senior Vice-President, ECD

Recall that in the hydrogen loop, presented in Figure 1-1, photons (light) are emitted by the sun and through photovoltaics produce electricity. The electricity can go directly to a battery or be used to electrolyze water. The hydrogen from the water then gets stored in ECD's solid hydrogen storage units. Finally, the hydrogen can be used either to power an internal combustion engine or a fuel cell. Stan has made a seminal contribution to the science at every step of the hydrogen loop. The next four chapters will discuss his work in each of these areas from photovoltaics to fuel cells, followed by a chapter on ECD's information technologies. Every attempt will be made to have these chapters be as simple and understandable as possible. More scientifically advanced readers are directed to the book's Appendices, where more in-depth and technically sophisticated papers on the various topics by Stanford Ovshinksy and his colleagues are offered.

Photovoltaics was an interest area for individual researchers and hobbyists for most of the twentieth century. With the OPEC oil embargo, the 1970s saw the first serious efforts to make photovoltaics a sustained energy generation industry. However, with the return to cheap oil prices, photovoltaics languished as an industry. From 1977 on, ECD, under Stan's direction, made numerous generations, each larger than the last, of its Ovonic multi-layered, thin film amorphous photovoltaic processor, utilizing its continuous web production methods which he had first pioneered in the Ovonic thin films he had used in the information field. As ECD made alliances and raised money, it was always toward his goal of having photovoltaics be competitive to fossil fuels, a world changing event.

All other approaches of significance were with batch process single band gap, single- or poly-crystalline material, hundreds of microns thick compared to Stan's half micron multi-band gap amorphous materials which utilized the full spectrum of the sun's available light. ECD is now reaping the benefits of having made a radical departure from the conventional crystalline approach.

The Science

Here's my understanding of photovoltaics (PV). First, an overview of crystalline silicon photovoltaic production technologies and products, then a look at Ovshinsky's amorphous, thin film photovoltaic cells. Most photovoltaic cells are made of refined silicon, which has been plentiful and is a good conductor of electricity. Research papers often say that silicon photovoltaic cells are "grown." What this means is that first a large amount of refined silicon is melted (at around 1250° C.), and then a small seed crystal is put into the melt and slowly pulled out. The liquid silicon attaches to the seed crystal as it is drawn out in a regular, crystallizing pattern that eventually forms a cylinder called a silicon ingot. That is what is done to "grow" a silicon crystal.

Once you have the ingot, it is first sliced into thin round wafers. Then, to make the wafer a solar cell, some small impurities must be put into the silicon wafers in order to make a so-called p-n junction. Why is a silicon p-n junction necessary?

A solar cell works when light falls onto the silicon crystal and an electron is excited by the energy in the light. The electron goes from a lower energy position (leaving behind a hole) to a higher energy position. This creates what is called an electron-hole pair, which consists of a positive and a negative charge. But in order for a solar cell to work, these positive and negative charges must be separated. The internal field of the p-n junction serves as the separation mechanism. These separated charges want to come back together, and the physicist allows that to occur through an external wire—a wire that connects the two sides of the junction. Of course, electrons moving through a wire is electricity.

There have been two advantages to this crystalline silicon solar cell approach: 1) the use of silicon is a very mature scientific field because of the many years of work with semiconductors, transistors, integrated circuits and the like, which are all made of silicon; and 2) silicon is abundant in nature (sand is oxidized silicon). However, in 2006, as solar cell production has significantly increased, the demand is exceeding the supply of refined silicon, thus increasing its cost.

The basic challenge for the crystalline silicon industry is cost. It takes a long time to grow the crystal. It is an energy intensive process because a lot of energy is used to heat the silicon to a very high temperature. Because of the way the ingot is sliced into wafers, a lot of material is lost, which adds to the cost. After junctions are imbedded into the cells, a large number of solar cells must be wired and connected to one another to form a solar panel. These processes are also costly. Another problem with silicon crystals is that they are very brittle and break easily. In order to protect the solar cell from the external environment, a glass sheet is placed over the array of cells. This adds both unwanted additional costs and weight. So cost, weight, and breakage represent crystalline silicon's Achilles' heels. Furthermore, the crystalline lattice has lattice mismatch with different crystals so it is impractical to be made as a triple-junction.

There are still other technical problems with crystalline solar cells. For example, if some leaves or a shadow covers a single (usually 6 inches in diameter) solar cell in a much larger array, the current produced by the entire array is reduced dramatically. This is because the individual solar cells are linked in series, and the current produced is limited by the cell producing the lowest current. Also, because of all the energy required to melt the silicon at the beginning of the "growing" process, the energy payback of crystalline silicon solar cells is estimated to range from four to seven years (rather than approximately seventeen months for the Ovonic amorphous silicon-germanium alloy cells).

Now that we know the strengths and weaknesses of the crystalline silicon industry's production process, let's turn to Ovshinsky's ECD amorphous, thin film photovoltaic cells. The first advantage of a thin film approach to depositing silicon on any substrate is a tremendous savings in material costs. While complex in practice, ECD's silicon deposition process is simple in concept. Essentially, a gas such as silane and/or germane is decomposed into silicon or germanium and hydrogen [Flourine is used for some critical layers.] with the silicon/germanium depositing on a stainless steel substrate and the hydrogen being pumped away. This occurs in a vacuum chamber, with the decomposition energized by a "glow discharge" created by very high frequency alternating voltages applied between parallel metal plates.

So now ECD has a very thin film on a substrate, instead of a sliced crystal, as its photovoltaic cell. Even though nine similar layers are deposited over one-another to create an advanced "triple-junction" photovoltaic cell, the total thickness is less than one-half micron (a "micron" is one-millionth of a meter) whereas the best crystalline cells must be about 200 microns thick, as thinner cells break too easily. Thus ECD's material costs are significantly lower.

The crystalline photovoltaic cell has a very regular pattern of atoms throughout the solar cell, while ECD's thin film has an amorphous atomic structure—that is, the atoms are deposited on the substrate in a random pattern. To make a very complex topic very simple, suffice it to say that there are some quantum mechanical truths that reveal that light is absorbed much more efficiently by a randomly ordered pattern of atoms than by a regular pattern (as in the crystalline solar cells). Thus, amorphous silicon can be easily deposited onto a substrate by a glow-discharge method to produce an efficient absorber of light energy that employs very little material.

Recall that with crystalline silicon cells, the junctions are created in a planned manner. With amorphous silicon cells, the atoms and the carriers of the light energy, the electrons and the holes, are randomly distributed. These random patterns produce many defects in the amorphous silicon. These defects gobble up the electrons and holes. Thus, while you've created the electrons and holes, you cannot easily get electricity from the thin film. So the challenge for ECD researchers was: How do you reduce the number of defects in the thin film solar material? Basically, you compensate for the defects by adding hydrogen/fluorine gas during the deposition process. This reduces the number of defects, and you can then obtain a good level of efficiency in the thin film. ECD's successful approach from the beginning was that it was able to reduce the defects in the thin film solar material.

Why are thin film, amorphous photovoltaic cells so unique? Ovshinsky said that amorphous materials can be stacked, layer upon layer, quite efficiently. Because of the random pattern of atoms, thin film is a very forgiving material. Thus, ECD developed its triple-junction thin film approach. Rather than having only one solar cell junction, there are three layers of materials, (two of them containing germanium) stacked one on top of another that create three junctions instead of one. This advantageous situation is not true for crystalline solar cells. If you have a single crystal silicon cell and you place it on top of a single crystal germanium cell, you will get a pretty defective interface. This is because the silicon has a certain lattice constant (i.e., the distance between the atoms). Germanium has a different lattice constant. Thus, if you attempt to grow one cell on top of another you get a lattice mismatch.

However, rather than having only one layer of solar cells in their arrays, ECD continuously lays down three layers of cells, one on top of the other, which do not appear as distinct layers (since they are inherently a part of the solid material), but as a solid. Therefore, in the solid there are three junctions instead of one. Further, each cell is atomically attuned to a different part of the light spectrum. The top cell is made of amorphous silicon alloy only, which captures the blue part of the light spectrum. The middle cell gets about 10% germanium added, which captures the green light. In the bottom cell, there is about 40% germanium, which captures the red light. This triple-junction structure is why ECD's photovoltaic cells capture energy from a broader range of the light spectrum than do crystalline cells.

Recall that standard photovoltaic cells work well under sunny conditions, but they deliver almost nothing on cloudy days. Similarly, under perfect operating conditions, traditional photovoltaic cells deliver energy well. However, should a shadow or some leaves fall on a crystalline photovoltaic array and completely cover one cell in the array's series of cells, the entire series will not produce electricity.

ECD's photovoltaic cells are not restricted by these limitations. It is important to consider the real-world effectiveness of a photovoltaic system in delivering electricity under the far-from-perfect conditions that present themselves in our daily lives. We should consider not only what percentage of light energy a particular system can extract under laboratory conditions (e.g. 9%, 12%), but also what amount of electricity is produced under real-world conditions. This former figure is kin to an automobile's EPA estimates of city and highway mileages; the latter is kin to your actual mileage achieved under real-world conditions. Which is more important to you, a car with a good mileage *estimate* or a car that *gets* good mileage?

In a study by Michael Schmela comparing nine types of photovoltaic cells, ECD's amorphous multi-junction photovoltaic cells produced much more total energy (which is what you pay for) than the eight other types of solar cells.[1] Similar real world results are reported in other studies conducted in Germany and in California.[2] Appendix 3, entitled "The Material Basis of Efficiency and Stability in Amorphous Photovoltaics," provides further discussion of the materials Stan has developed to capture energy from sunlight.

Machine Building

David E. Brown profiled "thirty-five inventors who helped to shape the modern world" for a book entitled *Inventing Modern America: From the Microwave to the Mouse.*[3] Here Stan rubbed shoulders with Henry Ford (assembly line), Steve Wozniak (personal computer), Wilson Greatbatch (implantable cardiac pacemakers), and their like. Stan was chosen for his pioneering work in amorphous photovoltaics and the fundamental changes that came from his introducing multi-junction, roll-to-roll, continuous web production machines (previously mentioned in Chapter 6) that made solar cells by the mile, and therefore could lead to making photovoltaics competitive to fossil fuels in producing electricity. Appendix 4, entitled "25/30MW Ovonic Roll-To-Roll PV Manufacturing Machines," includes pictures and descriptions of this remarkable machine.

Stan, who always was a scientist, started out his inventive career as a machinist, tool maker, and machine builder, all based on his inventive talents. He introduced new physics into metal cutting and new servo-mechanistic controls into a very old-fashioned industry. For example, his Benjamin automatic center drive machine (named after his father) was used in the automotive industry. Also, when the

Korean War started, the New Britain Machine Company manufactured his center-drive machines that produced steel cartridge cases many times faster than any existing machine. He always used new physics to make an entirely different machine tool than anyone had ever considered before with orders of magnitude improvements over conventional machines.

Stan was interested in building new industries and his aim even in those days was not to make incremental improvements to existing products but to create important new products that the world needed. For example, Stan felt that the automotive industry should not be using hydraulic power steering wherein the faster an auto went, the more dangerous the power steering was. In the early '50s he was director of research in the Amgears Division of the Hupp Corporation in Detroit, an automotive supplier which originally was the manufacturer of the Huppmobile. There Stan invented electric power steering. His servo-mechanistic power steering sensed the road and gave just enough (but no more) assist sufficient to meet the needs of driving under any conditions. He felt that the automotive industry could benefit from the use of low-cost sensors rather than relying on the strictly mechanical approaches that were utilized at the time. This was a very prescient approach to auto steering.

As Stan continued his work at ECD as a scientist and businessman, he never lost his love for machines and inventions. Most companies purchase machines and materials, which then enable them to produce their products. In contrast, Stan invents the new materials to build new products, he invents the products, and then he invents the production technology—all of which are based on his approach to amorphous and disordered materials. Thus, under Stan's leadership, the ECD teams design and build the production machines that will be required to manufacture their novel products (e.g., photovoltaic cells, nickel-metal hydride electrodes and batteries, solid hydrogen storage powders). The procedures and machines are developed, and the production processes necessary to create the new products are initiated and then debugged. Therefore, ECD actually creates new industries.

As mentioned in Chapter 1, demand for ECD's photovoltaic cells has been sufficiently high to warrant a doubling of its solar capacity, and in 2005, ECD made the decision to build a second 25/30 MW photovoltaic machine near the original Auburn Hills United Solar Ovonic plant. ECD owns 100% of United Solar Ovonic. The company is currently considering building new plants in the U.S., Europe, and Asia thereby again multiplying its solar capacity.

Stan feels that his greatest invention is building the teams of talented, creative and committed colleagues who then collaboratively become part of his inventive approach. He recognizes the latent abilities of his co-workers, and helps them to actualize their potential and flourish professionally. Looking at his patents, it is obvious that he includes as co-inventors all those who contribute. To Stan, the collegiality and collaboration needed to make great strides is a critical part of ECD's culture.

Stan leads ECD's machine building group which has been responsible for building many generations of machines. Their track record is truly amazing, and they can look forward to playing an even greater role in the future. Similar is the talent and leadership in all of the scientific and technical groups of ECD (for example, hydrogen, batteries, information). One is hard pressed to identify another company that spans the range of activities from materials creation to product sales as does ECD. Unique in the breadth and ambition of its work, ECD's objective is to put the twin pillars of our global economy, energy and information, on new foundations.

Appendix 3 Footnotes

[1]Schmela, M., "In Holland, the Sun Prefers Amorphous Modules." *Photon International*, November, 2000, pp. 10-11.

[2]"A Real-World Examination of PV System Design and Performance." Gregg Allen, Terrence Parker & Ron Swenson, United Solar Ovonic. Paper presented at the 31st Institute of Electrical and Electronics Engineers, Inc. Photovoltaic Specialist Conference and Exhibition, January 3-7, 2005, Lake Buena Vista, Florida.

[3]*Inventing Modern America: From the Microwave to the Mouse.* David E. Brown, 2002, Cambridge, MA: MIT Press.

Appendix 4

Presented at PVSEC-15, Shanghai, China, October 10 - 15, 2005

25/30 MW Ovonic Roll-To-Roll PV Manufacturing Machines

Stanford R. Ovshinsky and Masat Izu

Energy Conversion Devices, Inc., 2956 Waterview Drive, Rochester Hills, Michigan 48309; email: mizu@ovonic.com

Abstract: Energy Conversion Devices, Inc. (ECD Ovonics) is building a new a-Si thin film PV plant, which is a clone of the existing 25/30 MW United Solar Ovonic plant with improvements. The plant, which will be built in Auburn Hills, Michigan, for United Solar Ovonic, will be completed and commissioned for production in 2006. The proprietary production machines have been developed, engineered, and constructed by ECD Ovonics' Production Technology and Machine-Building Division (Machine Division). The machines are automated and designed to produce large, flexible rooftop PV modules that use triple-junction triple-bandgap a-Si alloy solar cells produced on stainless steel. When planned improvements are incorporated into the production line, the plant is expected to produce 30 MW PV modules per year with a module efficiency above 9%

Key Words: Amorphous Silicon, Roll-to-Roll PV Manufacturing, Building Integrated PV (BIPV), Flexible PV Modules

1 Introduction

Photovoltaic (PV) energy generation is one of the fastest growing industries in the world. The ECD Ovonics proprietary multi-junction, triple-bandgap, continuous web, thin-film technology is the ultimate solution for PV energy production [1]. ECD Ovonics, through its wholly owned subsidiary, United Solar Ovonic, has set a new standard for PV products. Compared to traditional crystalline PV, ECD Ovonics' thin-film PV can provide more overall energy since its triple-bandgap technology can capture up to 30% more per rated watt. Our proprietary photovoltaics, manufactured by the miles, are:

- lighter,
- more durable, and
- more attractive (Figs. 4-5) than crystalline products.

In addition, our PV products can be produced in high volume from abundant and affordable raw materials. ECD Ovonics' roll-to-roll process is a most cost-effective process for high-volume production [2].

The United Solar Ovonic flexible thin-film photovoltaic material is made on proprietary high-output, football field-sized roll-to-roll machines (Fig. 2) developed by ECD Ovonics' Machine Division. The Machine Division

- has developed, designed, built, installed, started-up, and optimized the latest United Solar Ovonic roll-to-roll PV production plant;
- has over 25 years PV technology experience from R&D and pilot-scale to large-scale automated manufacturing through eight generations of PV production equipment;
- develops, designs, and fabricates production equipment and pilot lines for all ECD technologies: hydrogen, battery, etc.; and
- has been chosen by General Electric to develop roll-to-roll manufacturing for OLED lighting products.

2 Specifications of Machines

Key specifications of the new 25/30 MW United Solar Ovonic PV production plant include:

- Annual Production Capacity: 25 MW (30 MW when fully optimized), or approximately 4 million ft^2/yr.
- Substrate: Rolls of 14 inch wide, 8500 foot long, 5 mil thick stainless steel (Fig. 3).
- Device Structure: Two layers of backreflector, nine layers of a-Si alloys, and a layer of ITO (Fig. 1).
- Real-time in-line device performance monitoring.
- Lamination: Tefzel/EVA polymer encapsulation.

3 Solar Cell Manufacturing Line

The Ovonic production line [3,4,5] includes a :

Roll-to-Roll Deposition Line consisting of a
- Washing Machine,
- Backreflector (BR) Deposition Machine,
- a-Si Alloy Deposition Machine, and an
- ITO Deposition Machine.

The Automated Module Assembly Line, includes a:
- Roll-to-Sheet Cutting Line,
- Cell Line,
- Interconnect Line,
- Lamination Line, and
- Finishing/Testing Line

4 ECD Ovonics Solar Cell Structure

Figure 1 shows the structure of the ECD Ovonics solar cell.

Grid		Grid	
Transparent Conductive Oxide			Sputtering
P3	Nanocrystalline Si Alloy		PECVD
I3	a-Si		PECVD
N3	a-Si Alloy		PECVD
P2	Nanocrystalline Si Alloy		PECVD
I2	a-Si/Ge Alloy		PECVD
N2	a-Si Alloy		PECVD
P1	Nanocrystalline Silicon Alloy		PECVD
I1	a-Si/Ge Alloy		PECVD
N1	a-Si Alloy		PECVD
Textured Metal/ZnO Back-reflector			Sputtering
Stainless Steel Substrate			

Fig. 1. Structure of a-Si Solar Cells.

5 Diagnostic Systems for the Roll-To-Roll Machines

The online non-contacting diagnostic systems [6] for the Ovonic roll-to-roll processors are summarized in Table I.

Table I. Diagnostic Systems for 25/30 MW Line.

Processor	Diagnostic System	No.	Measurement
BR	Scatterometer	1	Specular/diffuse reflection
	Reflectometers	2	ZnO thickness
a-Si	Reflectometers	15	Thickness of each n-, i-, and p-layer
	PVCD	4	Component and device electrical properties
ITO	Film Conductivity	1	ITO conductivity
	Reflectometers	5	Film thickness/uniformity
	PVCD	1	Device electrical properties; degree of physical shunts

Fig. 2 .25/30 MW Ovonic Roll-to-Roll PV Manufacturing Machine

Fig 3.   Roll of a-Si solar cell material.

6 Acknowledgements

The authors thank Herb Ovshinsky and his group for many years of contributions in designing and constructing the ECD Ovonics production machines. Also, we would like to express our thanks to Dr. Scott Jones, Dr. Vin Cannella, Dr. Tim Ellison, Dr. Joe Doehler, and Dr. Hellmut Fritzsche along with their collaborators for contributing the design and technical specifications for the machine. We also express our gratitude to Dr. Subhendu Guha, Kevin Hoffman, Gary Didio, Jon Call, and Dr. Prem Nath for their assistance on this project.

Fig. 4. A United Solar Ovonic BIPV roofing system helps power Grand Valley State University's 22,500 ft² Michigan Alternative and Renewable Energy Center.

Fig. 5. United Solar Ovonic was chosen to provide a building-integrated photovoltaic roofing system for the Beijing New Capital Museum. *Photo courtesy of Beijing New Capital Museum.*

7 References

[1] S. R. Ovshinsky, *Proceedings of the International PVSEC-1*, 1988, p.577.

[2] M. Izu, S.R. Ovshinsky, SPIE Proc. 407 (1983) **42**.

[3] S. Guha, J. Yang, A. Banerjee, K. Hoffman, S. Sugiyama, S. Call, S.J. Jones, X. Deng, J. Doehler, M. Izu, H.C. Ovshinsky, *Proc. 26th IEEE PV Specialist Conference*, Anaheim, CA, 1997, p.607.

[4] S.R.Ovshinsky, R. Young, W. Czubatyj, X. Deng, Semiconductor with Ordered Clusters, U.S. Patent 5,103,284, April 7, 1992.

[5] S.R. Ovshinsky, S. Guha, C. Yang, X. Deng, S. Jones, Semiconductor Having Large Volume Fration of Intermediate Range Order Material, U.S. Patent 6,087,580, July 11, 2000.

[6] T. Ellison, Proc. 28th IEEE PV Specialist Conference, Anchorage, AK, 2000, p.732.

A Roadmap to our Energy Future

Our need for energy has never been greater. Yet, burning more hydrocarbons will not solve our energy problem. Step-by-step, we are moving from the hydrocarbon economy of the past to the hydrogen-electricity economy of the future. Little by little, clean and renewable energy sources like wind, geothermal, tides, and most importantly solar are starting to be used in business and industry. Political forces, of course, impact the order and pace that this movement will take. Thus, forward looking businesses and politicians will be important in leading and guiding our steps to this hydrogen-electricity future. This book offers a roadmap to aid politicians and businesses as they plan and navigate the road to a clean, renewable and safe energy future.

About the Author

George S. Howard is a professor of Psychology at the University of Notre Dame. He has served as Chairman, Department of Psychology and Director, Laboratory for Social Research at Notre Dame, as well as the Joseph Morahan Director of College Seminar. He served as President, Division of Theoretical and Philosophical Psychology and President, Division of Humanistic Psychology of the American Psychological Association. He also was the 1998 winner of Notre Dame's *Faculty Award*. Author of 13 books and over 170 scientific articles and chapters, his specialties include philosophical psychology, research methodology, narrative psychology and environmental psychology.